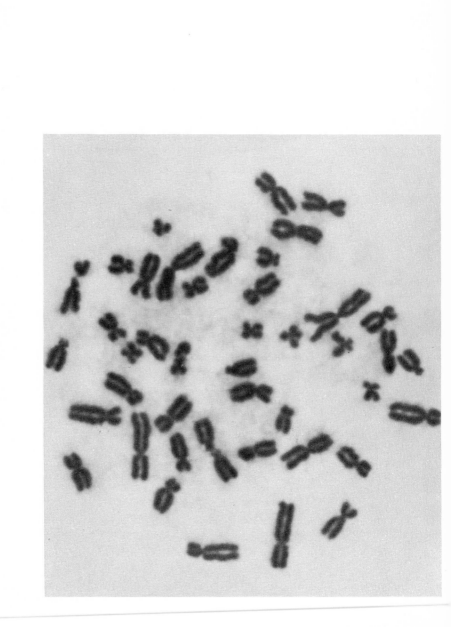

HUMAN
GENETICS

Victor A. McKusick
The Johns Hopkins University

Prentice-Hall, Inc.   Englewood Cliffs, New Jersey

FOUNDATIONS OF MODERN GENETICS SERIES

Frontispiece. Chromosomes of a single human white
blood cell in the metaphase stage of mitosis.

Current printing (last digit):
13 12 11 10 9 8 7 6 5 4

PRENTICE-HALL INTERNATIONAL, INC., *London*
PRENTICE-HALL OF AUSTRALIA, PTY, LTD., *Sydney*
PRENTICE-HALL OF CANADA, LTD., *Toronto*
PRENTICE-HALL OF INDIA (PRIVATE) LTD., *New Delhi*
PRENTICE-HALL OF JAPAN, INC., *Tokyo*

Foundations of Modern *Genetics*

Genetic research is alive with excitement and revolution-
ary advances. Important to the development of science
and to the evolution of social structure, genetic thought is
widening its impact on many areas: immunology, protein
chemistry, cellular physiology, developmental biology,
medicine, agriculture, and industry.

So many partnerships and such rapidly expanding
methodology demand a fresh approach to genetic training
—an approach attempted in this series.

The basic principles of genetics are few and simple. We
present them with enough description of accessory scientific areas to allow comprehension not only of the principles themselves but also of the types of experiments
from which the concepts have evolved. Such an approach
compels the reader to ask: What is the *evidence* for this
concept? What are its *limitations?* What are its *applications?*

The Prentice-Hall Foundations of Modern Genetics
Series presents the evidence upon which *current* genetic
thought is based. It is neither a history nor a survey of
all genetic knowledge. The short volumes make possible a
stimulating, selective treatment of the various aspects of
genetics at the intermediate level, and sectional divisions
allow free choice of emphasis in differently oriented college genetics courses.

The references cited in each volume and the current
research literature are the immediate sequels to this series,
but the true sequel remains in the hands of the alert
reader. He will find here the seed of more than one
enigma, the solution of which he, himself, may help bring
into man's comprehension sometime in the future.

SIGMUND R. SUSKIND
PHILIP E. HARTMAN

*McCollum-Pratt Institute
The Johns Hopkins University*

Preface

In this survey of human genetics, I have adopted a seemingly logical sequence that proceeds from the genetic material of man through the behavior of genes in kindreds, in individuals, and in populations to the implications of human genetics for human evolution, medicine, and society. I have placed strong emphasis on genetic analysis in man, and I have discussed in detail the methods now available: the pedigree method, linkage analysis, the chemical structure of proteins, and cytogenetic correlations.

The frequent use of rare, often abnormal, traits to illustrate the normal mechanisms of inheritance and gene action in man is not difficult to justify. Often the genetics of rare traits is less complicated than that of normal traits. Furthermore, aberrations from normal mechanisms are frequently valuable clues to the nature of the normal physiologic mechanisms. "Treasure your exceptions!" was the sound advice given by William Bateson (1861-1926), an early student of Mendelism. In 1657 William Harvey, who discovered the circulation of the blood, expressed the same idea in espousing the study of rare diseases:

> Nature is nowhere accustomed more openly to display her secret mysteries than in cases where she shows traces of her workings apart from the beaten path; nor is there any better way to advance the proper practice of medicine than to give our minds to the discovery of the usual law of Nature by careful investigation of cases of rarer forms of disease. For it has been found, in almost all things, that what they contain of useful or applicable nature is hardly perceived unless we are deprived of them, or they become deranged in some way.

There is a tendency to underestimate the usefulness of man as an object for genetic study. It is true that human genetic analysis is hampered by long generation time and small families; however, it is an advantage that anatomic, chemical, physiologic, and pathologic descriptions of phenotype in man are both extensive and intensive. Many physicians and workers in paramedical professions collect information of genetic significance that can be exploited by competent students of the science. Biochemical genetics was first studied in man—by Archibald Garrod (1857-1936), a London physician—in the early years of this century. Unfortunately the experience and conclusions in man did not enter the mainstream of genetic thought and theory until the 1940's. In man about sixty traits are known to be determined by genes, most of them probably nonallelic, on the X chromosome. The list represents the largest group of genes located to one chromosome in any metazoan other than *Drosophila*. *Homo sapiens* ranks with *Mus musculus, Drosophila, Zea mays, Neurospora crassa, Aspergillus nidulans, Escherichia coli*, and bacteriophages as a favorite organism for study by geneticists.

In general, studies in other organisms have laid the foundation for interpretation of the genetics of man. Mainly through a combination of studies in other organisms (in which more refined genetic analysis is possible) with those in man (in which phenotypic analysis is often more detailed), human genetics has been able to make its greatest contributions to the science of genetics. The science of human heredity cannot depend, however, only on extrapolation from findings in other species. Some aspects can be studied conclusively only in man. The example of sex determination in man, which is quite different from that in many other extensively studied forms, notably *Drosophila*, leads one to agree, although for different reasons, with Pope: "The proper study of mankind is man."

Genetics is to biology what the atomic theory is to the physical sciences. Human genetics has implications not only for all aspects of the science of man, but also for the cultural, political, and social aspects of human activity. Man has profited greatly from his knowledge of the genetics of the "economic" plants, animals, bacteria, viruses, and fungi. Although control of his own genetic future to a comparable extent has not yet been feasible, an understanding of his own genetics has been notably useful in some areas. For example, the dramatic advances in surgery, such as that on the interior of the heart, would have been hampered, if not impossible, without transfusion of large volumes of blood from other individuals. Knowledge of the manifold genetic differences in blood types among individuals made such transfusions safe.

Great areas of ignorance about the detailed genetics of many of the important variable attributes of man, e.g., intelligence, are all too obvious. However, an attitude of optimism for long-range accomplishments is justified on the basis of the progress made to date. I hope the reader is challenged by the gaps in our knowledge and catches from this brief survey some of the excitement of discovery in the rapidly advancing field of human genetics.

V.A.M.

Contents

Historical Introduction

Before 1900, when Mendel's observations of the 1860's were rediscovered, simple patterns of inheritance in man were observed. The traits were, naturally, obvious ones such as polydactyly (extra fingers), hemophilia, and color blindness. For example, in Berlin in the 1750's Maupertuis (1689-1759) described the autosomal dominant inheritance of polydactyly and discussed segregation in terms prophetic of Mendelism. The essential features of X-linked recessive inheritance of hemophilia were described in three unrelated New England families by Otto in 1803, by Hay in 1813, and by the Buels in 1815. In 1820, Nasse, a physician in Bonn, formally outlined this pattern of inheritance, later referred to as Nasse's law. Much earlier the Talmud made a provision for dispensing with circumcision in newborn males whose older brothers or maternal uncles had displayed a bleeding tendency. In 1876, Horner, a Swiss ophthalmologist, described the X-linked recessive pattern of color blindness.

Inheritance in a pattern we now recognize as autosomal recessive—the occurrence of a trait in multiple sibs, the offspring of normal parents, especially when the parents were related—was described in 1814 by Joseph Adams, who was far ahead of his time in his understanding of the dynamics of genetic disease. Further evidence of the importance of studying the biologic consequences of con-

1

sanguineous marriages is found in Bemiss' investigation, reported to the American Medical Association in 1857.

The twin method for separating the effects of heredity and environment was suggested by Francis Galton in 1876, although at first he was not clear about the distinction between monozygotic (identical) and dizygotic (nonidentical) twins. Along with his concept of regression Galton also initiated studies of quantitative genetics, that is, polygenic inheritance.

Shortly after the rediscovery of Mendelism in 1900, Archibald Garrod, on the advice of William Bateson, interpreted the pattern of inheritance of alkaptonuria (a metabolic disorder in which a substance called alkapton is excreted in the urine, which turns black on standing) in Mendelian recessive terms and recognized the significance of parental consanguinity. W. C. Farabee was one of the first to trace an autosomal dominant trait (in this case, brachydactyly, or short fingers) through a family and interpret its distribution specifically in Mendelian terms. In 1911 Thomas Hunt Morgan and E. B. Wilson of Columbia University demonstrated that the characteristic pattern of inheritance of hemophilia and of color blindness is consistent with the location of the responsible genes on the X chromosome.

Man was the first organism in which biochemical genetics was studied. From studies of alkaptonuria and certain other hereditary disorders, in 1908 Garrod, the London pediatrician mentioned above, developed his inspired concept of "inborn errors of metabolism." George Beadle, who in 1958 shared the Nobel Prize in Physiology and Medicine for his contributions to biochemical genetics, pointed out that his one-gene–one-enzyme hypothesis was really implicit in Garrod's work and was actually formulated by Garrod in essentially the same terms.

Also in 1908, G. H. Hardy, a mathematician at Cambridge University, and Wilhelm Weinberg, a physician in Stuttgart, independently laid the foundation of population genetics with what has been designated the Hardy–Weinberg law. Again the stimulus to the development came from human genetics—a consideration of the distribution of Mendelizing traits in human populations. In the early days of Mendelism it seemed to some that a dominant trait should increase in frequency and replace the recessive trait. "Why," it was asked, "does not everyone have brachydactyly?" Hardy and Weinberg considered gene frequency (actually *gene* was not yet a generally used part of the vocabulary) the most important aspect of population genetics. They showed, furthermore, that if disturbing factors were not operating, one would expect the frequency of genes and the traits for which they are responsible to remain constant from generation to generation. Weinberg is responsible for other contributions in the statistical methodology of human genetics—the Weinberg method for estimating the proportion of twin pairs that are monozygotic, and the Weinberg method for correcting for bias of ascertainment in estimating the proportion of sibs expected to be affected by an autosomal recessive trait.

In addition to the concepts of single-factor inheritance, Mendel formulated the concept of multifactorial inheritance, i.e., the additive effects of more than one gene pair. His crossing of white-flowered beans with purple-flowered beans resulted in an intermediate F_1 generation and an F_2 generation that displayed flowers ranging in color from purple to white. Early in this century a controversy raged, especially in England, between the biometricians such as Francis Galton and Karl Pearson and the exponents of Mendelism, such as Bateson, over the nature of inheritance in man. The Galton school had been studying quantitative traits such as intelligence and stature before the rediscovery of Mendel's works, whereas the Mendelists in the early years after 1900 were concerned with the inheritance of discontinuous traits. The two approaches were considered incompatible until 1918, when R. A. Fisher (1890-1962) demonstrated that multiple pairs of genes, each behaving in a Mendelian manner, account for the findings of the biometricians on quantitative traits. In that discussion Fisher introduced the term *variance*.

In the 1920's and 1930's important contributions to the theory of population genetics and evolution were made by R. A. Fisher and J. B. S. Haldane in England, by Sewall Wright in this country, and by Gunnar Dahlberg in Sweden. These workers and others, such as Fritz Lenz, Lancelot Hogben, and Felix Bernstein, have contributed greatly to the statistical methodology of human genetics, for example, the methods for segregation analysis, linkage analysis, and estimation of mutation rates.

The Atomic Age has been accompanied by an intensified study of the genetic effects of radiation. Although precise information must come from organisms available in large numbers for investigation under controlled conditions, estimation of human mutation rates and other studies of human populations have been stimulated.

In recent years, and especially in the last decade, there has been a great increase in appreciation of the importance of genetics in understanding diseases of man. Major contributions to human genetics have come from that part of the discipline that is called *medical genetics* because of its concentration on inherited pathologic traits. In biochemical genetics the primary role of gene action in protein synthesis has been elucidated through the work of Linus Pauling, Vernon Ingram, and others on hemoglobin variants. In 1959, by studies of the sex-chromosome constitution in sex anomalies, the mechanism of sex determination in man was shown to be different from that in *Drosophila*. Other chromosomal anomalies are being discovered; the first and most impressive of these was the one responsible for Mongoloid idiocy as described by Jérôme Lejeune in 1959. As recently as 1956 the true diploid chromosome number of man was established as 46, not 48, by J. H. Tjio and Albert Levan and by Charles Ford and John Hamerton.

The concept of genetic polymorphism, as expounded by E. B. Ford in 1940, is relatively new. Other than color blindness, however, the first discontinuous human trait that is now recognized as a genetic polymorphism was discovered by Karl Landsteiner in 1900, about the same time that Mendel's experiments were rediscovered. This was the ABO blood-group system. Since that time eleven other major blood-group systems, one of them X-linked, have been discovered, and have provided some of the clearest examples of the operation of Mendelian principles in man. Discovery in 1941 of materno-fetal incompatibility for the Rh blood groups uncovered a whole "new" category of genetically conditioned disease.

The polymorphism for ability to taste phenylthiocarbamide (PTC) was discovered in 1931. The recent search for other genetic polymorphisms of man has surged ahead through the use of diverse methods for showing immunologic, physicochemical, and enzymatic variations in proteins. The starch gel electrophoresis method that Oliver Smithies devised in 1955 has proved especially useful in revealing protein differences.

By the very definition of the term *polymorphism* (see p. 60) selection must be one of the main factors involved in the creation of polymorphisms if not in their maintenance. The role of selection in shaping the genetic constitution of man has been studied with increasing interest since the demonstration by A. C. Allison in 1954 of the role of malaria in maintaining the high frequency of the gene for sickle hemoglobin in populations of West Africa.

The eugenics movement, which antedated the rediscovery of Mendelism, has as its laudable objective an "improvement" of the species. The movement has, however, often brought ill repute to human genetics and has, in the opinion of most, impeded the progress of genetics as a science. There is not enough scientific information on which to base recommendations for large-scale eugenic action. Perversion of eugenics in the racist philosophy of the National Socialist regime of Germany undoubtedly caused a significant setback. Despite our present knowledge of human genetics, most scientists in the field consider insight so vague—and perhaps the morality of man so underdeveloped—as to make any significant eugenic measures inordinately risky.

Five Nobel Prizes in Physiology and Medicine have been awarded to workers in the area of genetics.

1934   Thomas Hunt Morgan (1866-1945), for research on the nature of the gene

1946   Hermann Joseph Muller (1890-   ), for discovery of the induction of mutation by X ray

1958   George Wells Beadle (1903-   ) and
Edward Lawrie Tatum (1909-   ), for contributions in biochemical genetics; and
Joshua Lederberg (1925-   ) for discovery of sexual recombination in bacteria

1959   Arthur Kornberg (1918-   ) and
Severo Ochoa (1905-   ), for studies of the chemistry of DNA and RNA

1961   James D. Watson (1928-   ),
Francis H. C. Crick (1916-   ), and
Maurice H. F. Wilkins (1916-   ), for elucidation of the intimate structure of DNA

By way of summary, my personal list of the ten most significant discoveries in human genetics follows. These are discoveries that were made predominantly in man but are applicable in other animals.

(1) The twin method was first developed by Galton in 1876.

(2) In the early years of this century Garrod focused attention on genetic blocks in chains of metabolic reactions.

(3) In 1908 Hardy and Weinberg focused attention on gene frequency as the pertinent variable in population genetics. They elaborated the fundamental principle on the basis of which factors leading to change in gene frequencies could be analyzed.

(4) Landsteiner initiated the study of simply inherited polymorphic traits in man by his discovery in 1900 of the ABO blood-group system. (Color blindness was, of course, discovered earlier.)

(5) The role of infectious disease in shaping the genetic constitution of man was suggested by E. B. Ford, J. B. S. Haldane, and others. The first clear evidence for such a role was provided by A. C. Allison in 1954, in his study of the relationship of malaria and the gene for sickle hemoglobin.

(6) In 1959 Lejeune and his colleagues first discovered a chromosomal aberration to be the basis of a congenital malformation in man —Mongoloid idiocy in this case.

(7) The role of the Y chromosome in sex determination in man was discovered by C. E. Ford and P. A. Jacobs and their colleagues in 1959.

(8) The role of the gene in determining the amino acid sequence of a protein was discovered in 1957 by Vernon Ingram who studied the difference between normal hemoglobin A and sickle hemoglobin of man.

(9) In 1961 several workers simultaneously suggested that one X chromosome in the normal female is relatively inactive genetically (the Lyon hypothesis). See page 72 for further explanation.

(10) In 1959 the first specific chromosomal aberration as the basis of malignant neoplastic disease of man was discovered in a form of leukemia by Peter Nowell and David Hungerford. See p. 24.

References

Boyer, S. H., IV, ed., *Papers on Human Genetics.* Englewood Cliffs, N.J.: Prentice-Hall, Inc., 1963.

Garrod, Archibald E., *Inborn Errors of Metabolism.* Reprinted with a supplement by Harry Harris. London: Oxford University Press, 1963.

McKusick, Victor A., "Walter S. Sutton and the Physical Basis of Inheritance," *Bull. Hist. Med., 34* (1960), 487-97.

———, "Hemophilia in Early New England," *J. Hist. Med., 3* (1962), 342-65. A follow-up of four kindreds in which hemophilia occurred in the pre-Revolutionary period.

Motulsky, A. G., "Joseph Adams (1756-1818), a Forgotten Founder of Medical Genetics," *AMA Arch. Inter. Med., 104* (1959), 490.

Pearson, Karl, *The Life, Letters and Labours of Francis Galton,* 4 vols. London: Cambridge University Press, 1914-30.

The Chromosomes of Man

In man as in other organisms, the hereditary material, DNA, is carried by the chromosomes. Somatic, or body cells, which have two of each type of chromosome, are diploid. In mitosis each chromosome is replicated and is represented in each of the two daughter cells. Gametes, or germ cells, which have one of each type of chromosome, are haploid and are produced in the process of meiosis. Segregation, assortment, and recombination occurring in the meiotic process are the basis of the characteristics of inheritance.

Until 1956 the diploid number of chromosomes in man was thought to be 48 instead of 46, and even the sex-chromosome constitution was in doubt. Improved methods for studying the mitotic chromosomes in somatic cells of man, however, have permitted a more accurate and more detailed description of the normal karyotype and the discovery of abnormalities responsible for certain congenital malformations. Two techniques in particular have helped greatly: (1) treatment of cell cultures with colchicine resulting in accumulation of dividing cells in metaphase, thereby assuring an adequate number of cells at a stage of division satisfactory for studying the chromosomes; (2) treatment with a hypotonic solution producing swelling of the cells and spreading of the chromosomes, thus facilitating their study. (See the volume on *Cytogenetics* in this series for further details on many aspects of this chapter.)

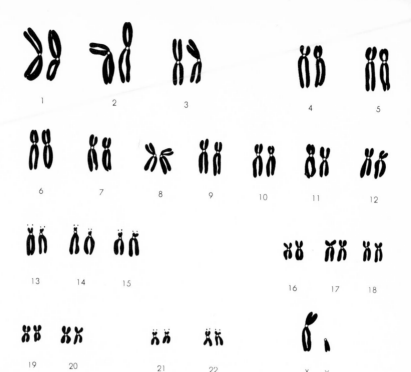

Fig. 2.1. The mitotic metaphase chromosomes of a somatic cell of a male, arranged in a karyotype. The Frontispiece is a photomicrograph of such chromosomes.

Fig. 2.2. The mitotic metaphase chromosomes of a somatic cell of a female, arranged in a karyotype.

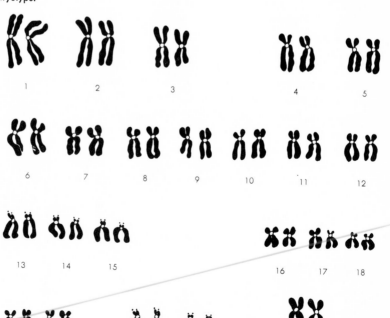

The cells used in these studies are obtained from bone marrow (aspirated from the sternum, for example), from bits of skin or fascia removed by biopsy, or from the white blood cells of a sample of venous blood drawn by the ordinary method of venepuncture. This last method, because of its simplicity, has obvious advantages. A step that has contributed to the success of the useful technique of blood culture is the addition of phytohemagglutinin. Derived from a bean, this material produces agglutination of red blood cells, thereby facilitating the separation of the white cells. In addition, phytohemagglutinin has associated with it a substance that stimulates cell division.

Stains such as aceto-orcein or Feulgen's, which are rather specific for the DNA of chromosomes, are used, and the preparations are examined by ordinary light microscopy. Individual chromosomes are cut out from enlarged photographs, matched in pairs of homologous chromosomes, and arranged in order of descending length (Figs. 2.1, 2.2).

The normal chromosome constitution

The normal diploid chromosome number of man is 46. The sex-chromosome constitution of the male is XY, and of the female XX. In addition there are 22 pairs of autosomes. In metaphase of mitosis each chromosome consists of two identical chromatids that separate in later phases, each to become one of the 46 chromosomes of one of the two daughter cells. The two chromatids are joined at the kinetochore (also called *centromere*, or *primary constriction*).

In man three classes of chromosomes (Fig. 2.3) are recognized according to position of the kinetochore and the resulting relative length of the arms, i.e., the parts of the chromosome on each side of the kinetochore. The three classes are: (1) median, or metacentric—kinetochore in an approximately central position with arms of equal length; (2) submedian, or submetacentric—kinetochore nearer one end than the other, resulting in one short arm and one long arm; and (3) acrocentric ("extremity center"), or subterminal—kinetochore near the end so that one arm is very short.

Fig. 2.3. Types of metaphase chromosomes. Note the satellites on the acrocentric chromosome. No chromosome of man is telocentric.

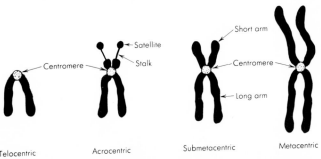

Telocentric   Acrocentric   Submetacentric   Metacentric

Placing the chromosomes in a karyotype is at best an approxima-
tion. Especially in the group comprising 6-12 plus X, and others such
as 21 and 22, one cannot be absolutely certain that the chromosomes
that seem identical on the basis of length and arm ratio are in fact
homologous. Several chromosomes can equally well be paired; moreover, there is no certainty that what is, for example, called chromosome
10 in one cell is the same as what is designated chromosome 10 in
another. The chromosomes can, however, be put into groups as shown
in Table 2.1.

Table 2.1. Human chromosome analysis by groups.

GROUP*	SIZE AND CENTROMERE POSITION	IDEOGRAM NUMBER	NUMBER IN DIPLOID CELL
I	Large; median/submedian	1-3	6
II	Large; submedian	4, 5	4
III	Medium; submedian	6-12 and X	15 (male) or 16 (female)
IV	Medium; subterminal	13-15	6
V	Small; median/submedian	16-18	6
VI	Smallest; median	19, 20	4
VII	Small; subterminal	21, 22 and Y	5 (male) or 4 (female)

* Groups IV and V are sometimes referred to as Group D and Group E, e.g., "Group
D trisomy." The other groups are, by this system, similarly indicated by letters A
through G.

The two sex chromosomes of the female are identical and are referred to as the X *chromosomes*. The X chromosome has a submedian
kinetochore, corresponds to Group III of the autosomes, and is usually
pair number 7 in terms of total length. The male has one X chromosome and a small acrocentric chromosome, the Y chromosome, that
sometimes cannot be differentiated with certainty from the other four
acrocentric chromosomes of the male. The Y chromosome tends to
vary, especially in length, from male to male, with close similarity in
males of any one family.

Another distinguishing feature of the normal chromosomes is the
presence of satellites, which are chromatin knobs connected to the short
arm of certain chromosomes by a stalk, or secondary constriction.
Satellites are found attached to five pairs of acrocentric chromosomes:
chromosomes 13, 14, and 15 (Group IV) and chromosomes 21 and 22
(Group VII). However, ten satellited chromosomes are almost never
identified in a single cell.

Secondary constrictions have also been identified in the long arms
of chromosomes 1, 9, and 16, and occasionally others. These constrictions also assist in the positive identification of individual

chromosomes. Sites of secondary constriction participate in the organization of the nucleolus, which serves some function in connection with messenger RNA, the intermediary in nuclear-cytoplasmic interaction, conveying the information encoded in the DNA of the chromosome to the sites of protein synthesis in the ribosomes of the cytoplasm.

Some chromosomes can be distinguished through autoradiography by a characteristic pattern in which new DNA is synthesized. Dividing cells incorporate the radioactive nucleoside tritium-labeled thymidine into the DNA of chromosomes.

Sex determination in man

In the late 1940's Murray Barr discovered a difference in the interphase somatic nuclei of males and females: a chromatin mass called the sex chromatin, or Barr body, is present in the normal female, but not in the normal male. This discovery and others in cases of sex anomaly were the beginning of our present understanding of the mechanism of sex determination in man and other mammals.

The Barr body (Fig. 2.4) can be identified in a significant proportion of cells in all tissues of the human female, and there is reason to think that it is present in essentially all female somatic cells, at least at some stage of interphase. Furthermore, in the human female the polymorphonuclear leukocytes tend to show "drumsticks," a characteristic pedunculated lobule of the nucleus (see Fig. 2.5). The simplest method for determining sex chromatin status (and therefore the method used in surveys) makes use of epithelial cells obtained by scraping the lining of the cheek with a tongue depressor. Thus, the XX sex-chromosome constitution of the normal female and the XY constitution of the normal male can be determined directly from karyotype analysis of somatic cells in metaphase (e.g., Figs. 2.1, 2.2), or indirectly from the sex chromatin and the leukocyte drumsticks.

Fig. 2.4. The Barr body, or sex chromatin. (*a*) Cells of the normal female have one Barr body as indicated by the arrow. (*b*) Cells of the normal male lack the Barr body. (*c*) Persons with three X chromosomes (the XXX or XXXY syndrome) have two Barr bodies.

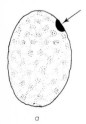

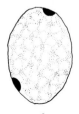

a   *b*   *c*

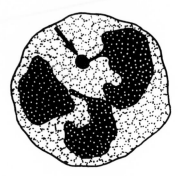

Fig. 2.5. The "drumstick" that can be identified in about 5 per cent of the polymorphonuclear leukocytes of the normal female.

But what is the critical difference between the normal male and female? Is the human male a male by default? Does the presence of two X chromosomes determine a female and the presence of one X chromosome determine a male? Or does the Y chromosome play an active role in determining maleness? The answers to these questions have come largely from the study of sex anomalies.

When the Barr technique was applied to sex anomalies of man it was discovered that certain persons had sex chromatin findings inappropriate to the phenotype. Specifically, persons with the Turner syndrome have external genitalia of female type but are chromatin negative, and persons with the Klinefelter syndrome are chromatin positive despite external genitalia of male type. (Examples of these two anomalies are shown in Figures 2.6 and 2.7, with a description of the phenotypic features.) The sex chromatin findings suggest a sex-chromosome abnormality, which is indeed found on study of the metaphase chromosomes: in most cases of the chromatin-negative Turner syndrome there are only 45 chromosomes and only one sex chromosome, an X. The sex-chromosome constitution is said to be XO ("X-Oh"). In the chromatin-positive Klinefelter syndrome 47 chromosomes are found, there being two X chromosomes and a Y. The sex-chromosome constitution is said to be XXY.

Any chromosomal aberration characterized by a deviation from the normal total number is known an aneuploidy. Polyploidy exists when the chromosome number is some simple multiple of the normal haploid number. For example, many liver cells are tetraploid with 92 chromosomes.

The Klinefelter syndrome occurs once in every 400 to 600 "male" births; the Turner syndrome is less frequent, occurring about once in

Fig. 2.6. The Turner syndrome. (a) The features are female external genitalia, short stature, webbed neck, low-set ears and typical facies, broad shield-like chest with widely spaced nipples and undeveloped breasts, small uterus, and ovaries represented only by fibrous streaks. In some cases coarctation of the aorta (a marked narrowing just beyond the mouth of left subclavian artery) leads to severe hypertension in the upper part of the body. Such has been corrected surgically in the patient illustrated here; note the surgical scar on the left side of the thorax. The patient is "chromatin-negative." (b) The karyotype of this patient, with 45 chromosomes and an XO sex-chromosome constitution. This photo appeared in *J. Chronic Diseases* (July 1960) and in *Medical Genetics 1958-1960* (Mosby, 1961); reproduced by permission of the editors of the *Journal of Chronic Diseases* and The C. V. Mosby Company.

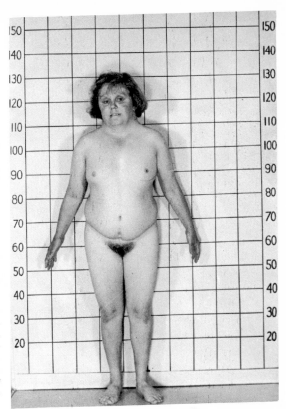

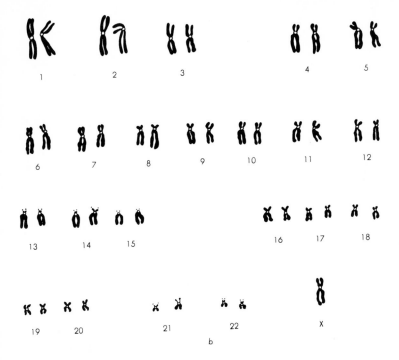

b

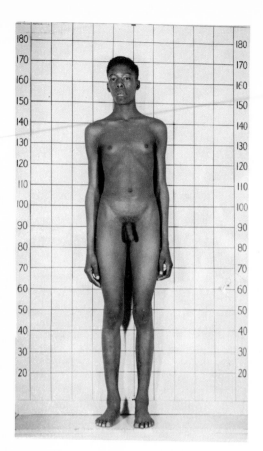

Fig. 2.7. The Klinefelter syndrome. (a) The external genitalia are of male type but the testes are consistently very small and body hair is sparse. Most of the cases have gynecomastia—female-like breast development. Patients tend to be unusually long-legged. They are "chromatin positive." (b) The karyotype of this patient, with 47 chromosomes and an XXY sex-chromosome constitution. This photo appeared in *J. Chronic Diseases* (July 1960) and in *Medical Genetics 1958-1960* (Mosby, 1961); reproduced by permission of the editors of the *Journal of Chronic Diseases* and The C. V. Mosby Company.

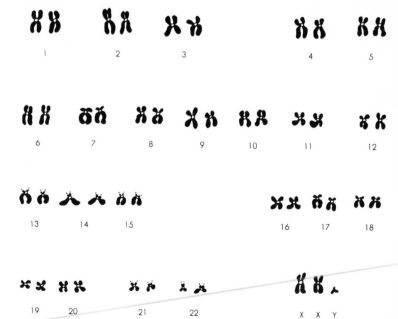

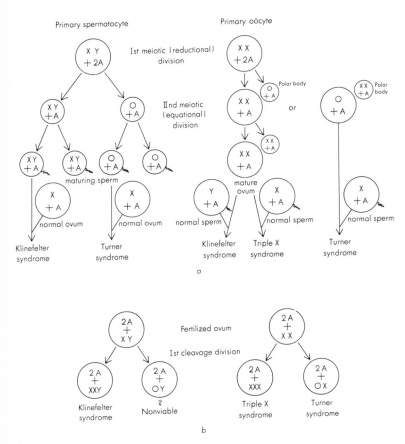

Fig. 2.8. Mechanisms by which aneuploidy of the sex chromosomes might develop. (a) Nondisjunction in gametogenesis. (b) Nondisjunction or chromosome loss in the zygote. Note the mechanism by which the nonmosaic XXY Klinefelter syndrome might arise from an XY zygote.

each 5,000 "female" births. There are several theoretically possible mechanisms by which these conditions might occur, and there is precedence in other organisms for suspecting the accident of nondisjunction either in one of the two meiotic divisions of gametogenesis in one of the parents or in the early mitotic divisions of the zygote. Figure 2.8 presents these mechanisms schematically.

Study of X-chromosome marker traits in the afflicted person and in both parents provides some indication of the origin of the X chromosomes in XO and XXY cases (Fig. 2.9). Color blindness has, for example, been observed in XO individuals whose parents both have normal color vision (Fig. 2.9a). Since color blindness is an X-linked recessive trait, it is concluded that the mother is a heterozygous carrier for color blindness, that she contributed to the offspring the X chromosome bearing the mutant allele for color blindness, that the case of Turner

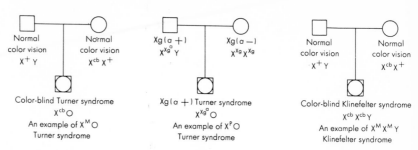

Fig. 2.9. Demonstration of the X^MO and X^PO states and of the X^MX^MY state by family studies.

syndrome is of the X^MO type, and that it is the paternal sex chromosome that is missing. Either the ovum was fertilized by a sperm without any sex chromosome or the paternal sex chromosome, either X or Y, was lost at an early stage, perhaps in the rearrangement of the male pronucleus that occurs in the time between the entrance of the sperm into the egg and completion of fertilization. Cases of X^PO Turner syndrome have been identified by means of the blood type Xg^a, which is an X-linked dominant (Fig. 2.9b). In these cases the maternal X chromosome is missing. The origin of the XXY Klinefelter syndrome has been investigated by a similar approach (Fig. 2.9c).

Other sex-chromosome anomalies have been discovered in recent years. One of these, phenotypically female, has two Barr bodies in the nuclei of buccal scrapings, and a sex-chromosome constitution of XXX. Another of these, phenotypically male, has two Barr bodies and a sex-chromosome constitution of XXXY. Other anomalies as indicated in Table 2.2 have been recognized. Many of these patients are mentally retarded and have been detected by sex-chromatin surveys in institutions for the retarded. The brain is such a delicately balanced mechanism that it is most vulnerable to being thrown out of kilter by chromosomal aberrations.

At least two principles emerge from the data outlined in Table 2.2.

(1) The maximum number of Barr bodies in any one cell is one less than the number of X chromosomes.

(2) The male sex phenotype is precisely correlated with the presence of a Y chromosome. In the absence of a Y chromosome the sex phenotype develops along female lines regardless of the number of X chromosomes present.

The mechanism of sex determination in man and in the mouse is quite different from that in *Drosophila* and many other nonmammalian forms in which the role of the Y chromosome is not the active one it is in most mammals. The mechanism in man parallels that in the plant *Melandrium*.

Table 2.2. Sex determination.

SEX PHENOTYPE		FERTILITY	NUMBER OF BARR BODIES	SEX-CHROMOSOME CONSTITUTION
Normal male	male	+	0	XY
Normal female	female	+	1	XX
Turner syndrome	female	−	0	XO
Klinefelter syndrome	male	−	1	XXY
Triple X syndrome	female	±	2	XXX
Triple X-Y syndrome	male	−	2	XXXY
Tetra X syndrome	female	?	3	XXXX
Tetra X-Y syndrome	male	−	3	XXXXY
Penta X syndrome	female	?	4	XXXXX

Origin of the Barr body

Further evidence that the Barr body is derived from *one* X chromosome is provided by two observations. (1) Cells in an early phase of mitotic division show that one X chromosome of the female stains differently from the other X and from the autosomes (Fig. 2.10a); this X chromosome is said to be heterochromatic. (2) In cultures of cells from the female, thymidine labeled with tritium (H^3) can be added. The thymidine becomes incorporated into newly synthesized

Fig. 2.10. (*a*) Heterochromatic X chromosome in prophase. (*b*) Late-labeling X chromosome in radioautographs using tritium-labeled thymidine. Courtesy of Dr. S. Ohno.

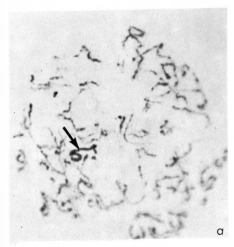

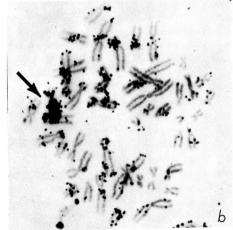

DNA of such cells. Asynchrony in DNA synthesis by the two X chromosomes can be observed by means of autoradiographs made of cells dividing in these cultures (Fig. 2.10b). The heterochromatic X chromosome synthesizes DNA late in the process of mitosis and is the X chromosome that constitutes the Barr body. This statement is based on the fact that the cells of persons with three X chromosomes (XXX or XXXY) have two heterochromatic X chromosomes, two late-labeling X chromosomes, and two Barr bodies; persons with four X chromosomes (XXXX and XXXXY) have three; and so on.

Information from other species suggests that heterochromatin is genetically inactive. The Lyon hypothesis, which will be discussed in Chapter 4, proposes that the Barr body is related to dosage compensation in man and other mammals, i.e., that it provides an explanation why the normal female with a double dose of X chromosome genes shows no greater effects than the normal male with a single dose. Other genetic observations are explained by the Lyon hypothesis. It should be noted that the X chromosomes in the germ-cell line of the female, that is, the two X chromosomes of the oögonia, do not display this cytologic differentiation (p. 28).

Abnormalities of the autosomal chromosomes

The first autosomal abnormality to be described in man was the one responsible for Mongoloid idiocy, or Down's syndrome. (See Fig. 2.11a for a description of this disorder.) All patients with this characteristic phenotype (Fig. 2.11b) have all or most of chromosome 21 triply represented rather than doubly; in most cases there is simple trisomy of chromosome 21, each cell containing three chromosomes 21 rather than two. It is impossible to be certain whether the trisomy involves chromosome 21 or 22 since they are morphologically identical, but it is reasonable to assume that only one of these pairs is involved and that in all cases it is the same pair. By convention and for convenience the twenty-first pair is considered the affected one.

Nondisjunction comparable to that described in the sex chromosomes appears to be the basis for the anomaly in Mongoloid idiocy. Older mothers are much more likely to have Mongoloid children (Fig. 2.12) than younger mothers. There is indirect evidence that the nondisjunction may occur either in the ovum during meiosis or in the early cleavage stages of the zygote; possibly the former is more frequently the case. If the latter possibility occurs, then the corresponding monosomic cells (cells with only one chromosome 21) probably die. (The Turner syndrome is a monosomic state involving the X chromosome; however, no monosomic state involving autosomes has yet been discovered. It is apparently more disruptive to have too few autosomes than it is to

Fig. 2.11. Down's syndrome, or Mongoloid idiocy. (a) The clinical features are mental retardation, a peculiarity in the folds of the eyelids suggesting the eyes of Mongoloid peoples (although in fact quite different), short stature, stubby hands and feet, peculiarity of the palm prints, and congenital malformations, especially of the heart. (b) The karyotype of a patient with Down's syndrome. It is uncertain whether the extra chromosome is a chromosome 21 or 22; by convention it is designated 21. This photo appeared in *Medical Genetics 1958-1960* (Mosby, 1961); reproduced by permission of The C. V. Mosby Company.

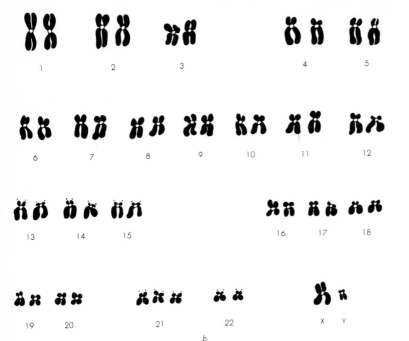

b

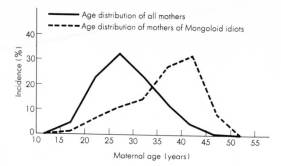

Fig. 2.12. Age distribution of mothers of Mongoloid idiots compared with that of all mothers. Based on data of L. S. Penrose.

have too many. In the X chromosome, special mechanisms of dosage compensation have developed, and monosomy or polysomy are relatively well sustained.)

Translocation of chromosomes 21 and 15 is another mechanism for Mongoloid idiocy. Such cases are found to have 46 chromosomes with two normal chromosomes 21, one normal chromosome 15, and an unpaired large chromosome that is interpreted as a fusion of at least part of a chromosome 21 with a chromosome 15 (Fig. 2.13a). In translocation cases, as in the more usual instances of trisomy 21, the genetic material of chromosome 21 is present in triple dosage. Cases of Mongolism with the usual trisomy 21 and those of so-called translocation Mongolism are phenotypically identical. When the parents of cases of translocation Mongolism are studied it is usually found that one parent, phenotypically normal, has only 45 separate chromosomes—one chromosome 21, one chromosome 15, and a large translocation chromosome composed of most of chromosomes 15 and 21 (Fig. 2.13b). The parent is phenotypically normal, as one would expect, since the genetic material is present almost in full and certainly not in excessive amounts. Providing the centromere of the translocation chromosome is that of chromosome 15, the gametes produced by such a parent are expected to be of at least four types with respect to chromosomes 15 and 21 (see Fig. 2.14).

(1) Normal 15 and 21, producing a normal zygote.
(2) Chromosome 15 alone, producing a zygote monosomic for chromosome 21—probably a lethal state.
(3) Translocation chromosome 15-21 and normal 21, producing a Mongol zygote.
(4) Translocation chromosome alone, resulting in a phenotypically normal individual with 45 chromosomes as in the parent.

Certain instances of multiple Mongoloid idiots in families (such as in sibs or cousins) have their basis in the translocation mechanism of

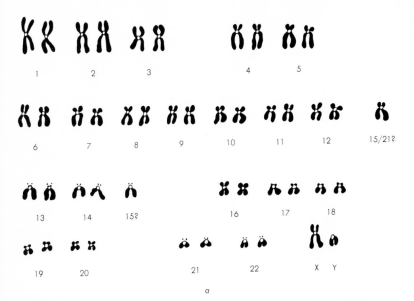

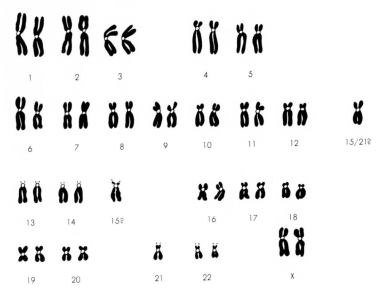

Fig. 2.13. (a) The karyotype of a patient with translocation Mongolism. Forty-six chromosomes are present with one normal chromosome 15 and two normal chromosomes 21, but in addition there is a large chromosome formed by translocation between chromosomes 15 and 21. (b) Karyotype of this patient's mother, who is phenotypically normal but has 45 chromosomes, one of which is a fused chromosome 15-21.

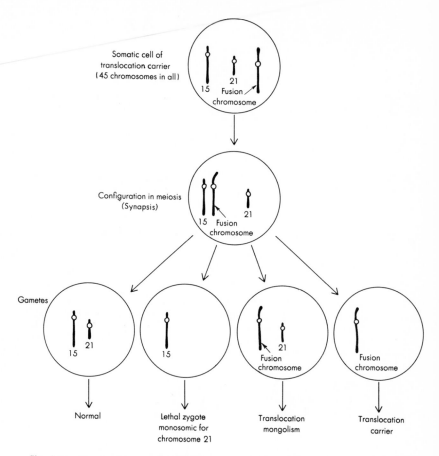

Fig. 2.14. The gametes produced by a carrier of the 21-15 translocation. Note that the translocation chromosome has one centromere, that of chromosome 15.

the 21-15 type. Mongoloid idiots with translocation of chromosome 21 to other chromosomes, e.g., 22, have also been observed. Furthermore, some Mongoloid idiots appear to have an isochromosome 21, that is, a chromosome consisting of the long arm of chromosome 21 in duplicate.

Female Mongoloid idiots have had offspring. The ova produced by a Mongoloid idiot with the ordinary trisomy 21 can be expected to be of two types with equal frequency: those that have one chromosome 21 and those that have two chromosomes 21. After fertilization an ovum of the latter type will develop into a Mongoloid idiot. In keeping with these expectations, both normal and Mongoloid offspring have been observed from Mongoloid mothers in about equal frequencies. If one monozygotic twin is a Mongoloid idiot, then the other is expected to be a Mongoloid idiot. Experience bears out expectation; probably almost all monozygotic twins are concordant for this trait, whereas very few dizygotic twins are concordant.

Mongoloid idiocy is by no means rare. It occurs once in each 500 or 600 births, being more frequent when mothers are older than the average. Mongolism is the most frequent single definable entity causing severe mental deficiency.

It is undoubtedly significant that no trisomy of the largest autosomes has been described and that it is one of the smallest chromosomes that is involved in Mongoloid idiocy. The trisomies of slightly larger chromosomes, one of Group IV (13-15) and one of Group V (17 or 18) lead to early death. The large chromosomes contain so much genetic information that the effects of overdosage are probably always lethal.

Mosaicism

A mixture of cells with different karyotypes is known as *mosaicism*. Some cases of the Turner syndrome have mosaicism of XO and XX cells, and some rare cases of Mongolism have trisomy 21 in some cells and a normal karyotype in others. Sometimes the karyotypes in mosaics are complementary, e.g., XO in some cells and XXX in other cells. Such mosaicism indicates that the accident of cell division took place in the zygote (or later) rather than in gametogenesis. Chimerism, a phenomenon similar to, but distinct from, mosaicism, occurs in dizygotic twins through exchange of blood cells *in utero* (see Chapter 5).

Abnormalities of chromosome structure

An isochromosome of the long arm of the X chromosome has been observed in some cases of chromatin-positive Turner syndrome. These persons have clinical features like those of the more frequent chromatin-negative XO Turner syndrome, but have only one normal X chromosome. The other X chromosome is replaced by a larger chromosome (the size of a number 3 chromosome) with a median kinetochore (Fig. 2.15a) ; this larger chromosome is thought to arise through transverse rather than longitudinal splitting of the centromere at the second meiotic division (Fig. 2.15b). The long-arm chromatids remain connected at the kinetochore and form the isochromosome. That the long chromosome indeed consists of duplicated long arms is supported by the identical pattern of autoradiographic labeling when tritium-labeled thymidine is added to cultures of cells in such cases. The patient has unusually large Barr bodies, and is trisomic for the long arm but deficient for the short arm of the X chromosome. Because of this

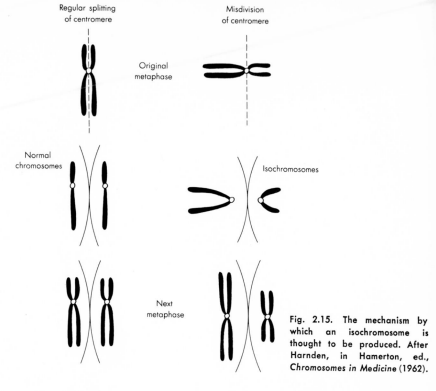

Fig. 2.15. The mechanism by which an isochromosome is thought to be produced. After Harnden, in Hamerton, ed., *Chromosomes in Medicine* (1962).

deficiency many of the features of the usual XO Turner syndrome are present. A presumed isochromosome of the long arm of chromosome 21 has been found in some cases of Down's syndrome.

Deletion of part of one X chromosome has been observed as the basis of some sex anomalies. Deletion of the short arm results in a clinical phenotype essentially identical to the ordinary XO Turner syndrome. As in the case of the isochromosome Turner syndrome (XX), the patient is chromatin-positive; however, in the deleted-X cases (Xx) the Barr body is unusually small.

Other abnormalities such as ring chromosomes, dicentrics, acentric fragments, and chromatid breaks have been observed in persons exposed to ionizing radiation or to radiomimetic agents, such as nitrogen mustard, that are used in treating some forms of cancer.

Chromosome changes in cancer

In many cases of a major form of leukemia, so-called chronic myeloid (or granulocytic) leukemia, a chromosomal aberration in the form of a deletion of part of the long arm of one of the four small acrocentric chromosomes (either 21 or 22), has been found. The abnormality is confined to the blood-cell line as studied in cultures of peripheral blood or bone marrow and is not found in other somatic cells, for example, those derived from skin.

In leukemia as in Mongoloid idiocy it is uncertain whether chromosome 21 or 22 is implicated. However, several observations have suggested that the same chromosome is involved, in different ways, in both Mongolism and leukemia: peculiarities in the shape of the nucleus of leukocytes occur in Mongoloid idiocy. The occurrence of leukemia in Mongoloid idiots is much more frequent than in the general population. Leukocyte alkaline phosphatase is higher than normal in Mongoloid idiots and is lower than normal in persons with myeloid leukemia.

The deletion of chromosome 21 in the white-cell line, the "cause" of many cases of chronic myeloid leukemia, is presumably acquired, not inherited, as in the other anomalies discussed earlier. Causes of the deletion are under study; exposure to X ray is probably a cause in some cases.

In summary, the chromosomal basis of certain congenital malformations, sex anomalies, and neoplastic diseases has been elucidated. Some structural abnormalities interpreted as deletions, translocations, and isochromosomes have been identified. As techniques improve, human cytogenetics will be able to detect more subtle changes that may prove to be more important to man than the obvious changes already discovered.

Cytogenetic mapping of the chromosomes of man

Mapping the chromosomes of man proceeds mainly by laboriously collecting linkage data on families (Chapter 3). However, cytogenetic approaches can help and can locate to specific chromosomes and parts of chromosomes the linkage groups established by family studies. General approaches that may be productive include the following:

(1) Deletion of part of one chromosome may "uncover" a recessive allele on the other chromosome.

(2) Familial distribution of marker traits may identify a particular locus with a particular chromosome. The following is a fictitious example: If the father of a trisomic offspring is blood type O, and if the mother and the offspring are both blood type AB, then the ABO locus must be on the chromosome involved in the trisomy, since the mother gave both alleles to the offspring. (See Chapter 4 for another possible explanation for such a finding, the Bombay gene.) Atypical frequencies of blood types in a trisomic population would be expected if the locus for that blood-group system is on the involved chromosome. However, it would be necessary to study a large number of subjects to demonstrate the effect.

(3) Dosage effects may point to the location of a particular gene on a particular chromosome. Leukocyte alkaline phosphatase activity is abnormally high in Mongolism (trisomy 21) and is abnormally low in cases of chronic myeloid leukemia with partial deletion of the long arm of chromosome 21. These findings may indicate the presence of a "leukocyte alkaline phosphatase locus" on the long arm of chromosome 21.

(4) Chromosomal peculiarities, such as unusually large satellites or the 15-21 translocation chromosome, can be used as one trait for family studies of linkage with other marker traits (Chapter 3). If a giant satellite on chromosome 15 showed close linkage with a particular blood-group system, then one would conclude that that blood group locus is on the short arm of chromosome 15.

(5) Somatic-cell genetics is in its infancy. The culture of human cells of known genotype promises to give useful mapping information. After inducing chromosomal aberrations and separating pure sublines, one may be able to study the biochemical characteristics of each and make inferences as to the location of genes controlling those characteristics.

As will become evident in the chapters that follow, genetic analysis in man, as compared with many other species, is hampered by the inability to do experimental matings and by the long generation time. Genetic analysis by study of the biochemical characteristics of human cells in tissue culture may be a partial substitute for experimental matings. Transformation, mutation, visible chromosomal changes—induced or spontaneous, and hybridization through cell fusion are only a few of the approaches that are being explored—already with some success —in human tissue culture.

The human chromosomes in meiosis

Up to this point, discussion has been confined largely to the chromosomes of somatic cells undergoing mitosis. However, a consideration of the chromosomes in meiosis, as well as other details of gametogenesis, is important, because chromosomal aberrations occur particularly in meiosis and point mutations of most genetic significance occur in the germ cells.

Testicular material (obtained after death or by biopsy performed on medical indications) can be prepared for study by methods similar to those used for the mitotic chromosomes. The chromosomes in cells at the first meiotic metaphase show an association of homologous chromosomes in pairs called bivalents (Fig. 2.16). Study of this material provides at least four types of useful information.

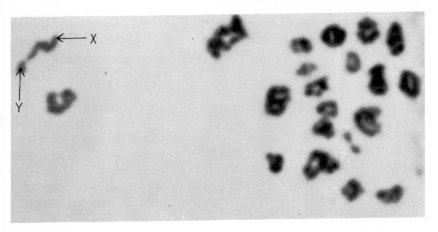

Fig. 2.16. The human chromosomes in meiosis in the male. The X and Y chromosomes are attached terminally at their short arms.

(1) The X and Y chromosomes either are not joined or show terminal association (Fig. 2.1). Side-to-side pairing as shown by other chromosomes does not occur. This cytologic discovery suggests that the X and Y chromosomes of man have little or no homologous segment and that crossing over between them does not occur. If any homologous segment did exist, genes carried on it would produce traits with a characteristic pattern of transmission in families, so-called partial sex linkage. There is, however, no substantial evidence from family studies that any trait in man is inherited in this manner.

(2) Chiasmas between homologous autosomes are visualized in meiotic material and can be counted. The formation of chiasmas may represent the physical exchange of chromosomal material between homologous chromosomes; in any event, chiasmas are correlated with genetic crossing over. *Chiasma* literally means "cross" and is the physical basis of the genetic crossing over that can be shown in family studies. The total number of chiasmas is a measure of the genetic length of the genome; the unit of map distance in genetic linkage studies is the crossover unit, or recombination fraction. Chiasma counts indicate that the total genetic length of the human chromosomes is approximately 3000 map units.

(3) Chromosomal rearrangements such as translocations and inversions are most easily recognized in testicular material from the configuration of the bivalents. For example, characteristic translocation figures are found in the male carrier of the 15-21 translocation chromosome.

(4) In man, as in many other species, the chromosomes in the pachytene stage of prophase show chromomeres—banding with char-

acteristic spacing and size. Only beginnings of a pachytene map in man have been made, and the goal of a complete pachytene map, correlated with a genetic map derived from linkage and cytogenetic studies, is yet to be achieved.

Oögenesis and spermatogenesis in humans

Human female germ cells multiply rapidly during early fetal life. Oögonia (the primordial germ cells of the female) cease to propagate after the fifth or sixth month of fetal life. The female infant is born with a full stock of oöcytes that must last for her entire reproductive life. Inventories of this stock have arrived at estimates of about 750,000 per individual female; however, a large proportion of these degenerate at various stages of oögenesis and at various times in the life of the female.

By about the time of birth the oöcytes have completed most of the prophase of the first meiotic division and then regress into a long interphase-like dictyotene stage during which the nuclear membrane remains intact and the chromosomes are visible as thread-like or net-like structures. The dictyotene stage lasts for at least 12 years and even as long as 50 years! During this period the DNA content of the oöcyte is tetraploid. (The DNA content of diploid interphase somatic cell nuclei is about 5.5×10^{-12} gm. per cell. Tetraploid liver cells and oöcytes in the long dictyotene stage have double this amount.)

The first meiotic, or reduction, division of the oöcyte is not completed until about the time of ovulation. Through the influence of pituitary hormone the dictyotene stage is terminated and resumption of meiosis is induced. The second, or equational, division of meiosis is usually completed only after the entry of sperm into the ovum. A polar body as one product of each meiotic division is extruded and lost. The second meiotic division separates the products of the crossing over that occurred between chromatids in the first meiotic stage. When the chromosome groups in the male and female pronuclei come together, fertilization is complete and the cell becomes a zygote. The process of fertilization usually takes place in the ampulla of the Fallopian tube. Implantation of the young human embryo occurs 6 to 7 days after ovulation.

Spermatogenesis differs from oögenesis in several important respects. The production of sperm is exceedingly abundant and the total number produced in the lifetime of a male is truly astronomical. Proliferation of spermatogonia does not begin until puberty, but thereafter usually continues throughout the lifetime of the male; oögenesis, on the other hand, is confined to the intrauterine life of the female. Four spermatids rather than one are produced from each spermatogonium;

no polar bodies are produced. The time for completion of the full cycle of spermatogenesis is about 64 days, and not from 12 to 50 years as in oögenesis. The two X chromosomes of the oögonia are isopycnotic, that is, they stain identically and stain like the autosomes, and by genetic and cytologic data they show crossing over between them. On the other hand, the X and Y chromosomes of the spermatogonium are heteropycnotic. They undergo early condensation and show at the most terminal association (Fig. 2.16). This mechanism has probably evolved to guarantee isolation of the critical male-determining genetic material.

The extent to which the genetic constitution of sperm is expressed in the phenotype of the sperm is a question of great biological and practical importance. For example, does the sperm carrying the allele for blood group A show this antigenetic specificity? The answer to this question is important to the matter of gametic selection in maintenance of the ABO polymorphism. Is there reduced fertility in couples of which one is homozygous for blood group A and the other homozygous for blood group B, and if so, might the reduced fertility be explained by the relative suppression of A-bearing sperm by anti-A antibody of the mother, or vice versa, of B-bearing sperm by anti-B of the mother? Among the sperm of AB men, are the A sperm at a relative disadvantage in women of blood type B, and B sperm at a disadvantage in women of blood type A? Full answers to these questions are not yet available. Selection may be operating on sperm, but the details are as yet largely unknown.

The ability to separate classes of sperm according to haploid genotype could have great practical importance. Control of the sex of the offspring is only one potential use. If one could separate into two classes the sperm from a male heterozygous for a gene causing a grave disease, one could perhaps avoid the transmission of that gene to the next generation—to the benefit both of his family and of the population in general. Unfortunately, however, even the dimorphism that should be most striking—that between X-bearing and Y-bearing sperm —is not reliably discernible by any method yet devised.

References

Ferguson-Smith, M. A., "Chromosomes and Human Disease," in *Progress in Medical Genetics*, Vol. I, Arthur G. Steinberg, ed. New York: Grune & Stratton, Inc., 1961.

McKusick, Victor A., "On the X Chromosome of Man," *Quart. Rev. Biol., 37* (1962), 69-175; also AIBS Monograph, 1964.

Montagu, M. F. A., ed., *Genetic Mechanisms in Human Disease: Chromosomal Aberrations.* Springfield, Ill.: Charles C. Thomas, Publisher, 1961.

Wilson, Edmund B., *The Cell in Development and Heredity*. New York: The Macmillan Company, 1925. A classic of biology.

Yerganian, George, "Cytologic Maps of Some Isolated Human Pachytene Chromosomes," *Am. J. Human Genet., 9* (1957), 42-54.

NOTE: *Lancet,* a medical journal published in London, has carried a large number of papers on human cytogenetics.

Genes in Kindreds

The chief method of genetic study in man is the observation of pedigree patterns, i.e., the patterns of distribution of genetic traits in kindreds. Since critically informative matings cannot be made by design, as is possible in experimental genetics, the human geneticist must rely on collections of families for information on the genetics of a given trait. The pedigree pattern provides information on the Mendelian principles of segregation and independent assortment; furthermore, it may provide information on allelism and linkage. Single-factor inheritance is also studied by pedigree patterns. Many important traits, such as intelligence, are, however, determined by many collaborating genes, each with a small effect. Here, too, analysis of intrafamilial similarities, essentially an extension of the pedigree method, is the principal approach.

Study of a particular trait in a family usually begins with an "affected" person who is referred to as the *proband,* or the *propositus* (female = *proposita*), or (especially by epidemiologists) the *index case.* The following conventions are useful in the construction of pedigree charts. The use of squares for males and circles for females predominates in this country and in continental Europe, whereas the symbols of Mars and Venus (♂ and ♀) are more generally used in Britain. Breeding records of other species generally list the female first in the representation of matings, i.e., ♀ × ♂. In human pedigree charts the usual practice is to place the male first, on the left, i.e., ☐─○. Some

prefer to set down the marital line thus: ⎣⎦ . Double marital lines

are used in case of consanguinity: ☐═○ . The proband is indicated by an arrow.

Sibs are indicated thus: ○₁ ☐₂ ○₃ ○₄ in chronological order

of birth. For economy of space, the number of normal sibs can be

indicated thus: ③ ② or ⑤ . Abortions or stillbirths are indicated

by small symbols: ● ; an indication of the sex, when known, by an

M or F, is valuable. Twins are indicated thus: △ or △

if monozygotic, △ , △ , or △ if definitely dizygotic,

and ☐ ? ☐ or ○ ? ○ if of uncertain zygosity.

Persons affected by the trait under study are indicated by blacking

in the symbols: ■ ● . More complicated devices can be used to

indicate the presence of multiple traits in the same individual or to

indicate the several manifestations of a single syndrome: ▦ , ▦ ,

etc. It is customary to use ⊙ to indicate the heterozygous female

carrier of an X-linked trait. The heterozygous parents of a person

affected by a recessive trait are sometimes indicated thus: ◧─◑ ,

especially if a partial defect is demonstrable in the heterozygote. Generations are numbered with Roman numerals, and range from the earliest at the top of the chart to the most recent at the bottom. Within each generation the individuals are numbered from left to right with arabic numerals. Thus, each individual in the pedigree is identified by a number, e.g., III 14. Sometimes spouses, e.g., those who are unrelated and marry into a kindred carrying an autosomal dominant trait, are indicated by a small letter following a number. Thus, III 14a would be the spouse of III 14, and III 14b, a second spouse.

Mendel's principle of segregation

In 1866 Mendel wrote, "Henceforth . . . those characters which are transmitted entire, or almost unchanged in the hybridization, and therefore in themselves constitute the characters of the hybrid, are termed the *dominant,* and those which become latent in the process *recessive"* (italics mine). The definition is precisely the one currently used if the word *heterozygote* is substituted for *hybrid.* Dominant traits are those that are expressed in the heterozygote. Recessive traits* are expressed only in the homozygote. It is implicit in the definition that the terms *dominant* and *recessive* refer, strictly speaking, to characters, not to genes. However, for convenience geneticists often speak, especially in population genetics, of a "recessive gene" or a "dominant gene."

The part of Mendel's definition, "almost unchanged in the hybridization," allows for phenotypic differences in the dominant character in the homozygote as compared to the heterozygote. The reader will recall that Mendel's classic experiments involved crosses between two homozygotes, one with the dominant character and one with the recessive character.

Many rare traits in man are distributed in families in characteristic patterns that are in accordance with the laws of Mendel. The specific pedigree pattern is dependent on whether the responsible mutant gene is located on one of the autosomal chromosomes or on an X chromosome, and also on whether the effects of the gene are evident in single dosage, that is, in the heterozygous state, or whether the gene must be present in double dosage (or the homozygous state) for expression. Depending on the type of chromosome bearing the gene in question, a trait is said to be either autosomal or X-linked. (The older term *sex-linked* is less satisfactory for several reasons, among them the fact that a holandric trait, determined by a gene on the Y chromosome, is also "sex-linked.") Depending on whether expression of the gene occurs in the heterozygous state or only in the homozygous state, a trait is said to be dominant or recessive, respectively.

Autosomal dominant inheritance

The first pedigree to be interpreted in terms of Mendelian

*As used by the geneticist, "trait" refers to any phenotype, whether disease or "normal variation," and whether in the homozygote (i.e., recessive) or heterozygote (i.e., dominant). In clinical medicine "trait" came to be applied to the heterozygous state of the sickle hemoglobin gene and by analogy is often used for the heterozygous state of other recessive genes. In the discussion here, "trait" will be used in the general phenotypic sense of the geneticist.

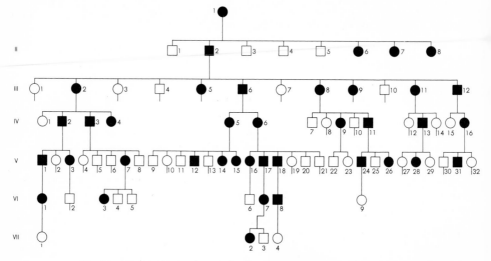

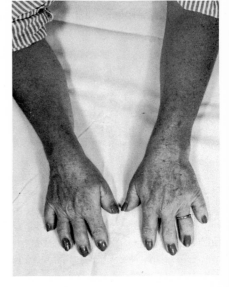

Fig. 3.1. (*above*) The family with brachydactyly first reported by Farabee in 1903; brought up to date in 1962. (*right*) Brachydactylous hands.

dominant inheritance was studied by Farabee when he was a graduate student at Harvard in the early years of this century. In this family the trait brachydactyly (short fingers) can be seen to be segregating (Fig. 3.1). Since it is rare it occurs in one parent only in each case. The unaffected spouses are omitted from the chart. On the average, half the sons and half the daughters of a man or a woman with brachydactyly are affected. This result is to be expected when the responsible gene is located on one of a pair of autosomes, since only one of each pair is contributed to a given offspring by the affected parent. The chromosome may with equal likelihood be either the one bearing the mutant gene for brachydactyly or the one bearing its normal, or so-called wild-type, allele.

In general, dominant traits are less severe than recessive traits. In part, an evolutionary or selective reason for this observation can be offered. A dominant lethal, i.e., a dominant mutation that determines a grave disorder making reproduction impossible, will promptly disappear. On the other hand, a recessive mutation, even if in the homozygous condition it precludes reproduction, can gain wide dissemination in heterozygous carriers.

Among children whose parents are both affected by a dominantly inherited trait and are both heterozygous for the responsible gene, the genotypic expectations are precisely as described by Mendel: one-fourth are homozygous affected, two-fourths heterozygous, and also affected, and one-fourth homozygous normal. Few autosomal dominant traits have ever been observed in the homozygous state. Some disorders that are relatively mild in the heterozygous state are lethal in the homozygous state; see Fig. 3.2 for a probable example. Probably few traits are completely dominant, that is, have the same phenotypic expression when the gene is in the heterozygous state as when it is in the homozygous state.

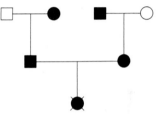

Fig. 3.2. Both parents had hereditary hemmorrhagic telangiectasia of about average severity. Their child was severely and lethally affected with multiple angiomatous malformations in many organs. This may have been an example of lethal homozygosity for a rare autosomal dominant gene. Redrawn from Snyder and Doan, *J. Lab. Clin. Med.*, **29** (1944), 1211.

Another characteristic of dominant traits is wide variability in severity, or "expressivity" (see Chapter 4). Sometimes the expressivity is reduced so much that the gene cannot be detected, at least by the methods currently available. When this is the case, the trait is said to be "nonpenetrant." So-called "skipped generations" sometimes occur in pedigrees of families with a dominant trait. In the "skipped" individual expressivity is so low that the presence of the gene is not recognizable from the phenotype, i.e., the trait is nonpenetrant in that person. Sometimes in taking a family history an apparent "skipped generation" turns up. However, when the "skipped" individual is subjected to close study, he in fact shows definite although mild manifestations.

Another phenomenon based largely on the wide variability in the severity of dominant traits is so-called "anticipation": the given hereditary disease manifests itself earlier, is more severe, and leads to earlier death in each successive generation, or at least in one generation than in the one immediately preceding it. This has been purported for myotonic dystrophy, a form of muscular dystrophy. Obviously the affected persons in generation I that have children are those at the milder end of the bell-shaped curve of severity, whereas *their* affected children, in generation II, will more nearly cover the whole range of severity. On the average, then, generation II is likely to be more severely affected than generation I by any measure, such as age at onset, degree of incapacitation, or age at death. Another source of bias leading to the artifactual phenomenon of anticipation is the fact that parent-offspring sets used in the calculations are often ascertained through the children. The more severely affected these children are, the more likely they are to come to attention. Anticipation has no genuine biological basis.

Autosomal recessive traits

Traits inherited as autosomal recessives (Fig. 3.3) likewise occur with equal frequency in males and females. When the trait is rare almost all the affected individuals have normal parents, but both are heterozygotes. Autosomal recessive inheritance is inheritance from both parents. Since related individuals are more likely to be heterozygous for the same mutant gene than are unrelated individuals, consanguineous matings, of first cousins for example, have a higher probability of producing offspring affected by a recessive trait. Viewed in another way, a greater proportion of the parental matings in families affected by recessive traits are likely to be consanguineous than is true

Fig. 3.3. Pedigree pattern of an autosomal recessive trait, myoclonic epilepsy. Based on Lundborg, 1912.

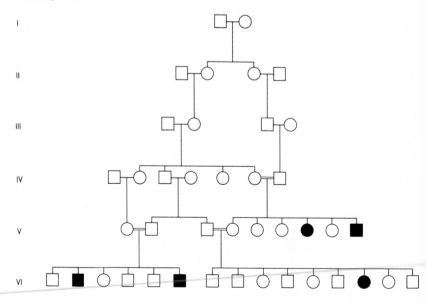

generally. The rarer the recessive trait, the higher the proportion of consanguineous parental matings. For more frequent autosomal recessive disorders (cystic fibrosis of the pancreas may be an example), there is little or no more consanguinity among the parents than expected by chance. In the case of a very rare recessive trait the occurrence of parental consanguinity may be the first clue to the fact that the trait is genetic.

Among the offspring of two heterozygous parents, one-fourth of males and females are expected to be homozygous and affected. However, in human genetics, sibships with both parents heterozygous are generally ascertained only through the occurrence in them of at least one affected member. Since there is usually no way to recognize the matings of two appropriately heterozygous parents who are so fortunate as to escape having affected children, a collection of sibships containing at least one affected child is a biased sample. In the ascertained families more than the expected one-fourth are affected.

If an individual affected by a recessive trait marries a homozygous normal person, none of the children will be affected, but all will be heterozygous carriers. If an individual affected by a recessive trait marries a heterozygous carrier of the same recessive gene, one-half of the offspring will, on the average, be affected, and a pedigree pattern superficially resembling that of a dominant trait will result. It was previously thought that two genetic forms of alkaptonuria existed—one inherited as an autosomal recessive and one as an autosomal dominant. Closer investigation revealed that the apparently dominant form was the same disease as the clearly recessive one. Because of inbreeding, homozygous affected individuals frequently mated with heterozygous carriers, and a quasi-dominant pedigree pattern resulted. See Fig. 3.4.

Dominance and recessiveness are somewhat arbitrary and artificial concepts. When our methods are sufficiently acute the effect of a recessive gene in the heterozygous state can often be recognized. Furthermore, a gene that has obvious expression in the heterozygous individual and is therefore considered dominant may have a different effect, quantitatively and even qualitatively, in the homozygous state. The gene for sickle hemoglobin (Hb S) and the states referred to as sickle-cell anemia and sickle-cell trait illustrate the arbitrary nature of the distinction. The phenotype sickle-cell anemia is recessive since a homozygous state of the gene is required (Fig. 3.5). Sickling, however, is a dominant phenotype, since the gene in heterozygous state is expressed. *Intermediate inheritance* is the term sometimes applied to this type of pedigree pattern. Intermediate inheritance means that the heterozygous individual is identical to neither of the homozygous individuals but is in a sense intermediate. *Incompletely dominant* or *in-*

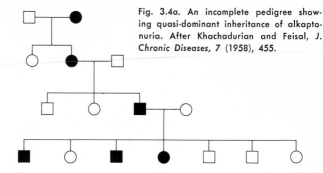

Fig. 3.4a. An incomplete pedigree showing quasi-dominant inheritance of alkaptonuria. After Khachadurian and Feisal, *J.
Chronic Diseases,* 7 (1958), 455.

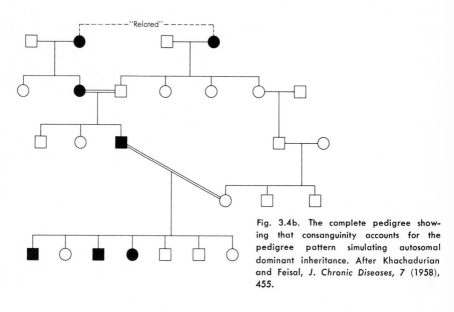

Fig. 3.4b. The complete pedigree showing that consanguinity accounts for the
pedigree pattern simulating autosomal
dominant inheritance. After Khachadurian
and Feisal, *J. Chronic Diseases,* 7 (1958),
455.

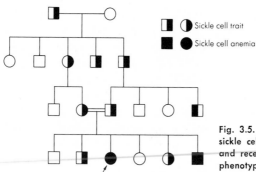

Fig. 3.5. Pedigree of a kindred with
sickle cell anemia showing that dominance
and recessiveness are characteristics of the
phenotype, not of the gene.

completely recessive are yet other terms used for this intermediate situation.

Codominance is the term used for characters that are both expressed, or jointly expressed, in the heterozygote. For example, persons with the blood group AB demonstrate the effects of both the gene for antigen A and the gene for antigen B. Neither is recessive to the other. Similarly, the genes for different hemoglobins are both expressed if the method for demonstrating the phenotype is paper electrophoresis, such as in a person with both hemoglobin S and hemoglobin C. These examples of codominance again indicate that whether we view the phenotype as recessive or dominant is dependent largely on the acuteness of our methods for recognizing the products of gene action.

X-linked inheritance

Like autosomal traits, those determined by genes on the X chromosome may be either dominant or recessive. The female with two X chromosomes may be either heterozygous or homozygous for a given mutant gene; the trait in the female can demonstrate either recessive or dominant behavior. But the male with one X chromosome can have only one genetic constitution, namely hemizygous, and regardless of the behavior of the gene in the female, whether recessive or dominant, it is always expressed in the male.

The critical characteristic of X-linked inheritance, both dominant and recessive, is the absence of male-to-male, that is, father-to-son transmission. This is a necessary result of the fact that the X chromosome in the male is transmitted to none of his sons although it passes to each of his daughters.

X-linked recessive inheritance is illustrated in a classical manner by hemophilia. Queen Victoria was a carrier (Fig. 3.6). Since none of her forebears or collateral relatives were affected the mutation may have occurred in an X chromosome in the germ line in one of her parents or in her early embryonic stage. One of her sons, Leopold, Duke of Albany, died of hemophilia at the age of 31. Prince Albert, the consort of Victoria, can be exonerated since male-to-male inheritance is impossible. At least two of Victoria's daughters were carriers for hemophilia since several male descendants were hemophiliacs. In the Czarevitch, son of the last Czar of Russia, and in the princes of Spain the gene for hemophilia inherited from Victoria had considerable political consequences.

The pedigree pattern of an autosomal dominant trait tends to be a vertical one with the trait passed from generation to generation. The pedigree of an autosomal recessive trait tends to be horizontal, with affected persons confined to a single generation. The pedigree pattern

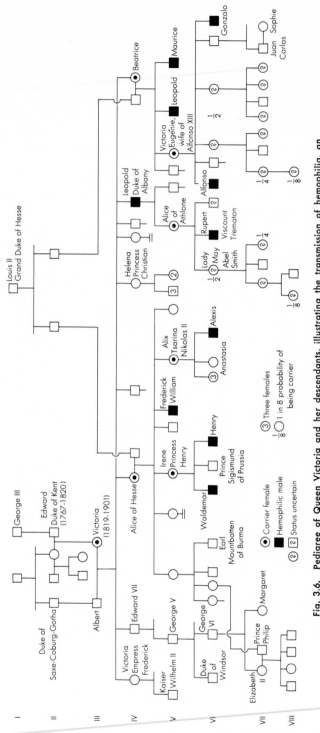

Fig. 3.6. Pedigree of Queen Victoria and her descendants, illustrating the transmission of hemophilia, an X-linked recessive trait.

40

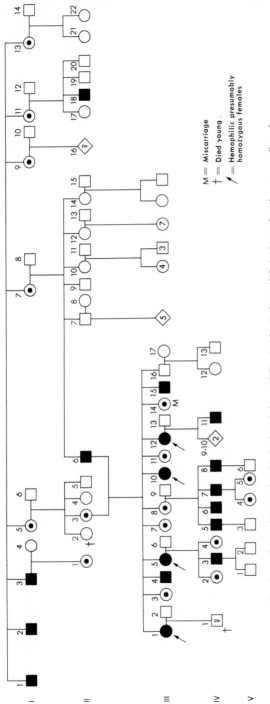

Fig. 3.7. The pedigree of a kindred with hemophilia A (classic hemophilia). Some females were affected (e.g., III 1) and there is apparent male-to-male transmission. However, affected males such as III 4 received the hemophilia gene from the carrier mother. Based on Gilchrist, *Proc. Roy. Soc. Med.*, 54 (1961), 813.

M = Miscarriage
† = Died young
⚬ = Hemophilic presumably homozygous females

41

of a rare X-linked recessive character tends to be oblique because the affection is almost exclusively of males and the transmission is to the sons of their normal, carrier sisters. William Bateson compared this pattern to the knight's move in chess. Tracing X-linked recessive characters through many generations is often difficult because the patronymic of affected persons usually changes with each generation.

Among the children of a male affected by an X-linked recessive trait, all sons are unaffected and all daughters are carriers (Fig. 3.7) —providing the mother is not affected and is not a heterozygous carrier. Father-to-son transmission of X-linked traits cannot occur.

To have hemophilia a female must be homozygous for this recessive gene; she must have received a gene for hemophilia from each parent. This can occur, and has been observed, when a hemophilic male marries a carrier female. As with other rare recessive traits this homozygous state is more likely to result from consanguineous matings (Fig. 3.7). Occasional females with hemophilia are "manifesting heterozygotes."

In man one can enumerate about sixty traits, most of them pathologic, that are X-linked. Most of them are X-linked recessives.

In X-linked dominant inheritance both males and females are affected and both males and females transmit the disorder to their offspring, just as in autosomal dominant inheritance. Superficially the pedigree patterns in the two types of inheritance are similar, but there is a critical difference. In X-linked dominant inheritance, although the affected female transmits the trait to half her sons and half her daughters, the affected male transmits it to *none* of his sons and to *all* of his daughters. One of the best studied X-linked dominant traits is vitamin D-resistant rickets, or hypophosphatemic rickets. The skeletal defect alone gives a pedigree pattern that tends to be inconclusive (Fig. 3.8a). However, when low blood phosphate is used as the trait for analysis the inheritance becomes clear (Fig. 3.8b). In all family studies the genetic analysis tends to be cleaner the closer the phenotype studied is to the primary gene action.

Effect of sex on gene expression

Note the distinction between sex-linked (X-linked) inheritance and sex-influenced or sex-limited autosomal inheritance. Baldness appears to be a sex-influenced autosomal trait. In the male "pattern baldness" behaves as an autosomal dominant, but in the female baldness behaves as a recessive since the gene must be in homozygous state for baldness to occur in women. Baldness can occur in a heterozygous woman who develops a masculinizing tumor of the ovary. Bald-

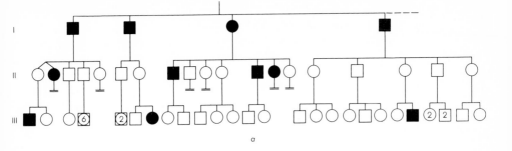

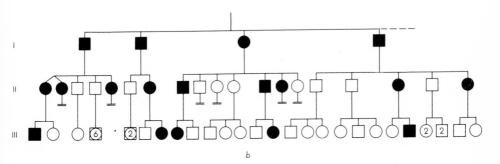

Fig. 3.8. Hypophosphatemic (or vitamin D–resistant) rickets. (a) When skeletal deformity is used as the phenotype the pedigree pattern is unclear. (b) When low serum phosphate is used as the phenotype the pedigree pattern is clearly that of an X-linked dominant trait. After Williams, et al., in Stanbury, Wyngaarden, and Fredrickson, eds., The Metabolic Basis of Inherited Disease (1960).

ness is a sex-influenced autosomal trait; the extreme case of sex influence is sex limitation.

It is difficult to distinguish X-linked recessive inheritance from sex-limited (i.e., male-limited) autosomal dominant inheritance if the nature of the disease is such that reproduction by affected males cannot occur. Figure 3.9 shows the pedigree of a family in which many males are infertile because of a testicular disorder. Note that since the

Fig. 3.9. The pedigree of a family in which many males have a testicular disorder that renders them infertile. Is this an X-linked recessive or a male-limited autosomal dominant trait?

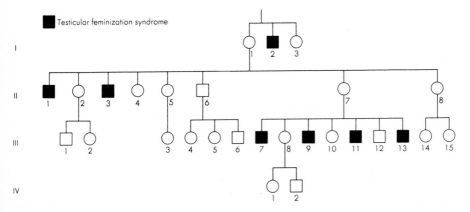

disorder can express itself only when tests are present (i.e., only in the male), autosomal dominant and X-linked recessive (or dominant) inheritance account for the pedigree pattern equally well.

The examples cited above illustrate Mendel's first law, that of segregation; traits are distributed in families as though the genes determining them segregate at meiosis. Alleles are alternative forms of genes that occur at the same genetic locus and determine alternative forms of the same trait. In several instances a considerable number of alternative genes have been identified at the same genetic locus, so-called multiple alleles. Any one individual can, of course, carry no more than two different alleles. In the ABO system, for example, the major alleles are A_1, A_2, B, and O (sometimes written I^{A_1}, I^{A_2}, I^B, I^O); these determine the particular blood group specificities that are designated by these letters.

Mendel's law of independent assortment

Mendel's second law is used by the blood-group geneticist whenever he undertakes to prove that a newly discovered blood-group antigen represents a "new" system and is not merely part of a previously known one. Whereas segregation is the behavior of genes at the same locus (alleles), independent assortment is the behavior of genes at separate loci (nonalleles). See Fig. 3.10. Alleles segregate; nonalleles assort.

Families of two or more children are needed to demonstrate independent assortment. The informative type of parental mating is the double backcross, in which one parent is heterozygous for both of the genes being investigated. The destination of this parent's genes in his children can be determined since the other parent has neither of

Fig. 3.10.   The genetic consequences of allelism, linkage, and independent assortment.

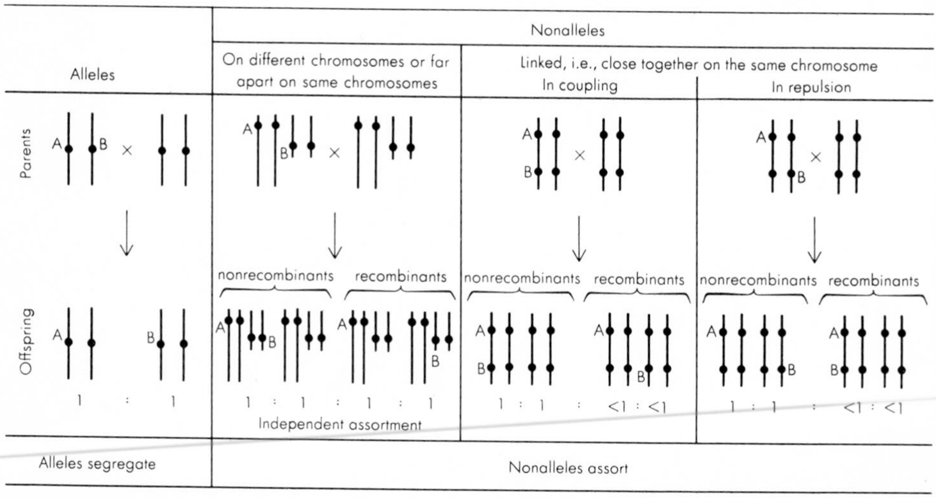

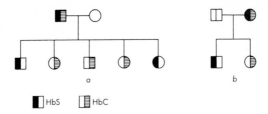

Fig. 3.11. Example of segregating alleles: the genes for hemoglobin S and hemoglobin C. (a) After Hays and Engle, *Ann. Internal Med.*, 43 (1955). (b) After Smith and Krevans, *Bull. Johns Hopkins Hosp.*, 104 (1959), 17.

them. The families diagrammed in Fig. 3.11 illustrate this approach. In these families two hemoglobin variants, Hb S and Hb C, occur. In the mating in which one parent has both and the other parent has neither aberrant hemoglobin, the first parent gives one or the other of the aberrant hemoglobins to each child. In no similar family observed to date has the "doubly affected" parent given both aberrant hemoglobins to a child and in none has he given neither to a child. Tentatively one can conclude from this evidence that the genes for Hb S and Hb C are allelic.

Figure 3.12 shows a different example from the hemoglobins. Again in this family, two variant hemoglobins occur, hemoglobin S and a hemoglobin called Hopkins-2. In this instance, unlike the Hb S and Hb C example, a parent with both Hb S and Hb Ho-2 does give both or neither aberrant hemoglobin to an offspring (witness III 1 and II 9). Thus, these hemoglobins are clearly determined by nonallelic genes.

Chemical evidence can provide information on allelism and nonallelism. In light of the current one-cistron–one-polypeptide thesis (see Philip E. Hartman and Sigmund R. Suskind's *Gene Action* in this series) allelic genes would be expected to determine variation in the same polypeptide, whereas nonallelic genes would be expected to be concerned with different polypeptides. Such is indeed the case:

Fig. 3.12. An example of the independent assortment of nonalleles: the genes for hemoglobin S and hemoglobin Hopkins-2. Based on Bradley, Boyer, and Allen, *Bull. Johns Hopkins Hosp.*, 108 (1961), 75.

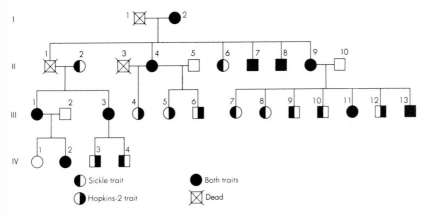

both Hb S and Hb C, which by the pedigree data (e.g., Fig. 3.11) are allelic, have a change in the β-polypeptide chain of hemoglobin; the difference of Hb Ho-2, which by the pedigree data (Fig. 3.12) is nonallelic with Hb S, resides in the α-polypeptide chain. The chemical and genetic analyses thus lead to the same conclusion.

For recessive genes also, nonallelism may be demonstrated by the familial pattern. Most genetic deaf-mutism (congenital deafness; deafness present from birth so that speech does not develop) is inherited as an autosomal recessive. Since phenotypically all such cases are identical, one might presume that genes at a single locus are responsible for all autosomal recessive deaf-mutism. Deaf-mute persons frequently marry deaf-mutes and the occurrence of pedigrees such as that in Fig. 3.13 demonstrates nonallelism. Specifically, since the children of the two deaf-mutes III 8 and III 9 had normal hearing, then the genes determining deaf-mutism in the part of the pedigree on the left (*a*) must be at a different locus than those determining deaf-mutism in the right-hand part (*b*). All the children of III 7 and III 9 are heterozygous at both loci, i.e., "doubly heterozygous."

Another approach to the problem of allelism and nonallelism involves the frequencies of the several genotypes in the population. This method was used by Bernstein in 1925 to prove that the ABO blood groups are determined by a system of multiple alleles rather than by a pair of genes at one locus determining A and non-A blood type and a pair at another locus determining B and non-B blood type.

Linkage relationships of genes can give evidence of nonallelism. For example, two varieties of hemophilia (hemophilia A, or classic hemophilia, and hemophilia B, or Christmas disease) are, by the evidence

Fig. 3.13. Deaf-mutism in a family observed in Northern Ireland. The condition present in the three generations of (b) is apparently due to the same gene, but the deafness in (a) is due to a nonallelic gene, since marriage of presumed homozygotes from the two lines (a, b) resulted in no affected offspring. After Stevenson and Cheeseman, *Ann. Human Genet.*, 20 (1956), 177-231.

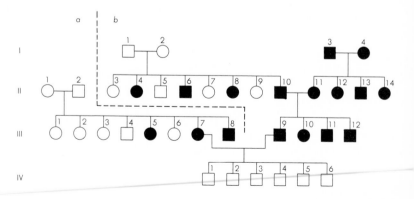

of pedigree pattern, X-linked. One might wonder if the genes responsible for the two varieties are allelic. Such is clearly not the case because hemophilia A is closely linked with color blindness, whereas hemophilia B is determined by a gene located a considerable distance from the locus for color blindness. The linkage method can prove nonallelism, but because of its crudity cannot prove allelism in man (see p. 55).

Linkage

Linkage is the occurrence of two loci on one chromosome sufficiently close together so that something less than completely independent assortment takes place. If two loci are on separate nonhomologous chromosomes, then independent assortment occurs. Even if the two loci are on the same chromosome, if they are sufficiently far apart, crossing over can result in independent assortment. See Fig. 3.10. Traits determined by genes at loci rather close on the same chromosome tend to be transmitted together from generation to generation. The principles of linkage are also discussed in Franklin W. Stahl's *The Mechanics of Inheritance* in this series.

The questions asked in linkage studies are the following: (1) Are the genetic loci occupied by the genes responsible for two traits on the same chromosome (or pair of chromosomes)? (2) If so, how far apart are the two loci? In practice the second question is answered first and the first question may follow directly. The distance between two loci determines the amount of crossing over that goes on between them. A measure of crossing over is provided by the proportion of recombinant or crossover individuals among the offspring of informative matings. If crossing over occurs to such an extent that 10 per cent of offspring of informative matings are of the recombinant type, then the two loci are said to be about 10 map units apart. If crossing over occurs to the extent that 50 per cent of offspring are of the recombinant type—a situation equivalent to independent assortment of Mendel's second law—then the two loci may be on different nonhomologous chromosomes or may be so far apart on the same long chromosome that independent assortment occurs through crossing over.

The analysis of linkage can be illustrated with the example of the Lutheran blood group and secretor trait (which is the secretion of ABO blood-group substance into the saliva; see p. 136). Families are collected in which the parental mating is of the double backcross type (one parent is doubly heterozygous and one parent is homozygous recessive). Four types of offspring are possible: Lutheran positive and secretor; Lutheran negative and nonsecretor; Lutheran positive and nonsecretor; Lutheran negative and secretor. Note that even if the

Lutheran and secretor loci are linked, no information is available at the start on whether the doubly heterozygous parent is in coupling or repulsion, i.e., has the dominant gene on the same chromosome (coupling) or opposite chromosome (repulsion). The offspring are lined up as shown in Table 3.1. Although the four types of offspring are

Table 3.1. Data on linkage of Lutheran and secretor.

PARENTS				
Phenotypes:	Lutheran positive, secretor		Lutheran negative, nonsecretor	
Genotypes:	$Lu^aLu/Se\ se$	$\times$	$Lu\ Lu/se\ se$	
OFFSPRING				
Genotypes:	$Lu^aLu/Se\ se$	$Lu\ Lu/se\ se$	$Lu^aLu/se\ se$	$Lu\ Lu/Se\ se$
Phenotypes:	Lutheran positive, secretor	Lutheran negative, nonsecretor	Lutheran positive, nonsecretor	Lutheran negative, secretor
SIBSHIP				
1	0	0	6	2
2	4	1	0	0
3	0	0	4	1
4	1*	0	1	5
5	0	1	0	1*
6	1	1	0	0
7	1*	1*	1	1
8	0	0	3	3
9	4	1	0	0
10	0	3	0	1*
11	1	3	0	1*
12	2	2	0	0
13	0	0	1	1
14	1	2	0	0
15	1	2	0	1*
16	1	1	0	2*
TOTAL	17	18	16	19

SOURCES: *Sibship 1, Mohr (1951); sibships 2, 3, Mohr (1953); sibships 4-6, Race and Sanger (1958); sibships 7, 8, Lawler and Renwick (1959); sibship 9, Metaxas et al. (1959); sibships 10-16, Greenwalt (1961).*
* Probable crossovers. In sibships 5, 7, and 16 the crossovers are arbitrarily designated. Total number of offspring is 70. Total number of crossovers is 9. Recombination fraction is 13 per cent.

represented in about equal proportion in the series as a whole, the distribution in individual families is far from equal. Those families with offspring only or predominantly to the left of the vertical line have the doubly heterozygous parent in coupling; the Lu^a and Se genes

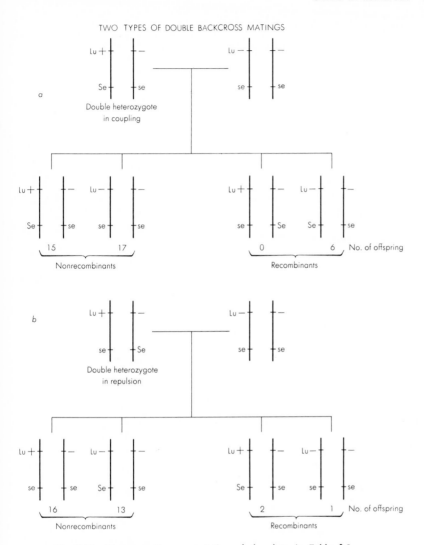

Fig. 3.14. Diagrammatic representation of the data in Table 3.1.

are on the same chromosome of a particular pair. Those families with offspring only or predominantly to the right of the vertical line have the doubly heterozygous parent in repulsion; the Lu^a and Se genes are on opposite chromosomes of a particular pair of homologs. Those individuals who fall on the side of the line opposite the majority are recombinants. In some cases, however, it is not certain which are recombinants and which are nonrecombinants, e.g., in families 5, 7, and 16. The data are presented in a different manner in Fig. 3.14.

Mapping of loci on the X chromosome

Analysis for autosomal linkage is difficult, both for the novice to understand and for the investigator to carry through in practice. X-linkage is somewhat more easily studied.

In studies of X-linkage the first of the two questions listed above (p. 47) is usually already answered in the affirmative—both loci are known from pedigree patterns to be on the same chromosome, the X. (This is not always the case, however, because male-limited autosomal dominant traits have a pedigree pattern identical to that of X-linked recessive traits; see p. 43.) The answer to the question of how far apart the loci are is provided by the phenotype of the sons of doubly heterozygous women. The one X chromosome of each son comes from the mother. X-chromosome crossing over can occur, of course, only in females. The father is irrelevant to the study of X-linkage—a circumstance fortunate for the study of populations with a high illegitimacy rate.

Male offspring of doubly heterozygous women will be of four types as indicated in Fig. 3.15, two noncrossover types and two recombinant or crossover types. If 2 out of 10 sons (20 per cent of sons) of such women are of the recombinant type, then it is concluded that the two loci are separated by about 20 map units. But how does one tell the recombinants from the nonrecombinants? As should be clear from Fig. 3.15, one must know the coupling phase—whether the two traits are in coupling or repulsion, whether the responsible genes are on the same or opposite X chromosomes in the doubly heterozygous

Fig. 3.15.   The grandfather method for mapping the X chromosome.

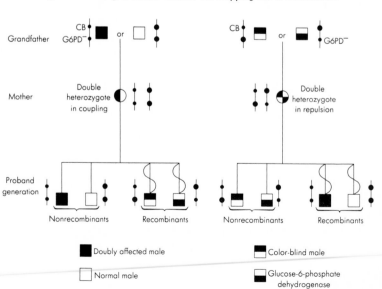

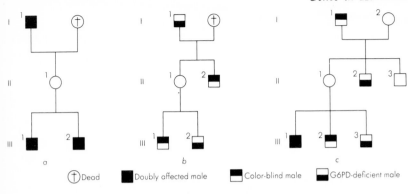

Fig. 3.16. Some pedigrees in which the linkage between color blindness and glucose-6-phosphate dehydrogenase deficiency was studied. There is one definite crossover. Can you identify it? Based on Porter, Schulze, and McKusick, *Ann. Human Genet.*, 26 (1962), 107.

mother—before the recombinants and nonrecombinants can be so labeled.

The coupling phase in the mother is determined from the phenotype of *her* father, as illustrated in Fig. 3.15. Here, of course, illegitimacy and the practical matter of availability of her father for study do become important considerations.

The so-called Grandfather Method for measuring the distance between X-borne loci can be illustrated with an actual study of the linkage of color blindness and deficiency of glucose-6-phosphate dehydrogenase in the red blood cell. Negro school boys were first screened for color blindness. Then all males in the sibship of the color-blind boys were tested for G6PD deficiency. Thereby, sibships were ascertained in which both X-linked defects occurred. In the great majority of these the mother was doubly heterozygous. (In only a minority was the mother homozygous for one or both traits. These uninformative families can be excluded by testing the phenotype of the mothers with regard to these recessive traits.) Next the coupling phase of the mother was determined in each instance from the phenotype of the maternal grandfather of the proband. Determining the recombination fraction was then merely a matter of counting up the proportion of recombinant individuals among the sons of the doubly heterozygous women. The pedigrees shown in Fig. 3.16 are some of those actually found. Only one instance of recombination is shown. The loci for color blindness and for G6PD deficiency are rather close together on the X chromosome, probably about 5 map units apart.

Figure 3.17 shows a tentative map of a segment of the X chromosome. In arriving at these approximate values the following five linkages have been tested: Xg blood group versus glucose-6-phosphate deficiency; glucose-6-phosphate deficiency versus color blindness; color blindness versus hemophilia A; Xg blood group versus color blindness;

and Xg blood group versus hemophilia A. The data are internally consistent, e.g., the sum of the distances separating Xg and G6PD, G6PD and color blindness, and color blindness and hemophilia is about the same as the distance separating the Xg locus and the hemophilia locus. Cytologic data suggest that the X chromosome is over 150 map units long; this is supported by the fact that many X-borne genes are not *measurably* linked to the Xg or color blindness loci. It is not known whether the mapped segment is on the short arm or the long arm of the X chromosome.

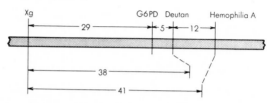

Fig. 3.17. Tentative linkage map of a segment of the X chromosome. The numbers given are the values for the map distance found in five separate studies. The recombination fractions have been converted to map distances by means of Kosambi's formula (see Fig. 3.18). The loci mapped are the Xg blood group locus, the G6PD deficiency locus, the deutan (green) color-blindness locus, and the classic hemophilia locus.

Difficulties in detecting autosomal linkage

The problems in detecting and quantitating autosomal linkage in man account for the slowness with which mapping of the human chromosomes has proceeded. Some of these problems are: (1) The traits for study must be monogenic and uncomplicated in their genetics, with no ambiguity in the scoring of "affected" versus "unaffected." (2) The traits for study must be dominant. (3) At least one of the traits must be frequent so that doubly heterozygous parents are found fairly often. (4) Man has 22 pairs of autosomal chromosomes. If each of the available marker loci were on a separate chromosome, there would still not be enough "to go around." Actually some of the long chromosomes can have independent assortment of widely separated loci through crossing over. From chiasma counts performed on the meiotic chromosomes it is estimated that the total genetic length of the autosomes is about 2,700 map units (p. 27). (5) The coupling phase of doubly heterozygous persons is often not known, although sometimes it may be inferred from the rest of the pedigree. Scarcely more than a dozen traits fulfill these requirements to qualify as marker traits. Various methods by which polymorphic traits are demonstrated are presented on p. 60. The markers useful in linkage work include several separate blood-group systems (e.g., ABO, Rh, Lutheran, MNSs, Duffy, Kidd, Kell), several serum protein polymorphisms (haptoglobin, transferrins, gamma globulin), and the ability to taste PTC.

Because of the difficulties in detecting autosomal linkage in man, few such linkages are known. The nail-patella syndrome and ABO blood groups are linked with a recombination fraction of about 10 per cent. One form of elliptocytosis and the Rh blood groups are linked with a recombination fraction of about 3 per cent. The Lutheran blood groups and secretor factor are linked, and have a recombination fraction of about 15 per cent (Table 3.2). One form of hereditary cataract is linked to the Duffy blood-group locus. The locus that controls synthesis of beta chains of Hb A and the one that controls the delta chains of Hb A_2 are very closely linked (see p. 65).

Other approaches to the demonstration of linkage

The close linkage of the beta and delta loci is indicated not only by classic family studies but also by three other types of evidence: (1) The beta and delta chains have close chemical similarities (in fact only 8 amino acids out of 146 are different), suggesting that they arose from a common ancestor through gene duplication and that they are probably contiguous. (2) A bizarre aberrant hemoglobin has been found, hemoglobin Lepore, in which the nonalpha polypeptide in part resembles the beta chain and in part the delta chain. Presumably the new gene (for Hb Lepore) arose through unequal crossing over that involved the two contiguous loci. (3) Two rare mutant alleles of the delta gene have been found. In all cases in which a delta mutant allele has occurred in the same individual as the sickle gene, a beta-gene mutant, the two genes have been in repulsion. This is interpreted as indicating very close linkage and insufficient time in generations for equilibration of the coupling and repulsion phases.

The methods just outlined can be resorted to in human genetics as substitutes for family data that are difficult to assemble in a volume that provides a critical answer on the question of linkage.

The relationship between recombination fraction and map distance is not one-to-one. The farther apart the loci, the more striking the discrepancy becomes, since double crossovers are scored as nonrecombinants. The unit of physical distance on the chromosome is referred to as the map unit, or centimorgan. The relationship between x (the recombination fraction) and map distance in centimorgans is diagrammed in Fig. 3.18.

Both the genetic and the cytogenetic methods (the latter having been discussed in Chapter 2) must be brought to bear on the problem of chromosomal mapping.

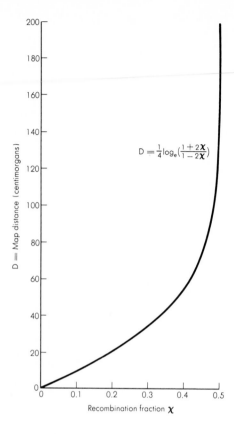

$$D = \tfrac{1}{4}\log_e\!\left(\tfrac{1 + 2\chi}{1 - 2\chi}\right)$$

D = Map distance (centimorgans)

Recombination fraction χ

Fig. 3.18. The relationship between recombination fraction (χ) and physical map distance in centimorgans. After Kosambi; courtesy of E. A. Murphy, Baltimore.

Association

Genetic linkage is quite different from blood-group-and-disease association. Association is the nonrandom occurrence of two genetically separate traits in a population. Before enough generations have passed for a chromosome to be minced up by the process of crossing over, association on the basis of genetic linkage may be observed, but linkage produces no permanent association in the population and most association has its basis in mechanisms other than genetic linkage. For example, the Lutheran blood-group locus and the secretor locus are known to be rather closely linked, being separated by about 15 crossover units (Table 3.1). Yet in any group of unrelated persons one Lutheran blood type does not occur more frequently with secretor than with nonsecretor. See Table 3.2, which shows that about 10 per cent of both secretors and nonsecretors were Lutheran positive. Furthermore, in the linkage data presented in Table 3.1, the numbers of persons with both traits, one trait only, or neither trait are about equal. No linkage is indicated and linkage becomes evident only when

Table 3.2. Independence of Lutheran and secretor phenotypes in 400 unrelated persons.

PHENOTYPE	$Lu(a+)$	$Lu(a-)$
Secretor	27	270
Nonsecretor	8	95
TOTAL	35	365

SOURCE: *Lawler and Renwick, "Blood Groups and Genetic Linkage,"* Brit. Med. Bull., 15 *(1959), 145-49.*

the individual families are studied. Conversely, blood group O and peptic ulcer of the duodenum show significant association (see p. 136). This is due to some physiologic peculiarity of the type-O person that predisposes him to peptic ulcer and is not due to genetic linkage.

Close linkage versus allelism

In human pedigrees close linkage is difficult to distinguish from allelism. The number of progeny from informative matings is small compared to the numbers on which recombination estimates can be based in experimental species. The problem arises in connection with the variant hemoglobins and the Rh and some other blood groups (p. 76).

References

Lawler, S. D., and J. H. Renwick, "Blood Groups and Genetic Linkage," *Brit. Med. Bull., 15* (1959), 145-49.

McKusick, Victor A., "On the X Chromosome of Man," *Quart. Rev. Biol., 37* (1962), 69-175. Also, AIBS monograph, 1964.

Renwick, J. H., "Elucidation of Gene Order," in *Recent Advances in Human Genetics*, Lionel S. Penrose and H. L. Brown, eds. Boston: Little, Brown & Co., 1961, pp. 120-38.

Genes in the Individual

Physiologic genetics is concerned with the way genes work, in collaboration with extrinsic, or environmental factors, to determine the phenotype. Biochemical genetics is essentially the same as physiologic genetics, because the objective of physiologic genetics is to understand gene action in biochemical terms.

The genotype is the genetic constitution of the individual. The phenotype is the character or trait or the composite of characters that is capable of being observed but that may be many steps removed from the genotype. The distinction might be compared to that between character and reputation. Genotype and character are what one really is; phenotype and reputation are what one appears to be.

Because it is so far removed from the genotype, the phenotype is not necessarily an indication of the genotype. Environmental factors can result in the same phenotypic change as a mutant gene. *Phenocopy* was Richard B. Goldschmidt's term for such environmentally induced mimics. Furthermore, different genes can result in the same phenotype. *Genetic mimic* (or *genocopy*) is the term for this phenomenon. For example, some hereditary disorders display autosomal dominant inheritance in some families, autosomal recessive inheritance in others, and X-linked inheritance in yet others. Elliptocy-

56

tosis (oval-shaped red blood cells), an autosomal dominant trait, is determined in some families by a gene rather closely linked to the Rh blood-group locus, whereas in other families the seemingly identical phenotype is determined by a locus not linked to Rh.

A trait may be highly variable from one person to another. Autosomal dominant traits in particular tend to show pronounced variability. *Expressivity* is the term that has been applied to this characteristic of a hereditary trait, and is equivalent to the grade of severity in clinical medicine. A population of persons of a particular genotype will fall into a bell-shaped normal distribution curve according to the expressivity of the hereditary trait determined by that genotype. A majority of "affected" persons have an intermediate grade of severity, whereas a few have severe affection and a few have mild involvement, perhaps sometimes so mild that the presence of the gene escapes detection. The curve is skewed in one direction or the other in the case of most traits. The basis for such variability in expression is partly environmental and partly genetic. The individual mutant gene primarily responsible for a trait does not operate in a vacuum, but rather against the background of the rest of the genome. In the case of autosomal dominant traits the presence of different wild-type alleles can modify the expression of the mutant gene. In the nail-patella syndrome, an autosomal dominant disorder, the grade of severity shows a much higher correlation between affected sibs than between offspring and affected parent. *Isoalleles* is the term applied to multiple wild-type alleles that appear to have identical phenotypic effects except when observed in heterozygous combination with a mutant allele, in this case that for the nail-patella syndrome.

Genetic traits that are subject to considerable modification by the effects of genes other than the primary one and also by environmental influences may not be recognizable in some individuals despite the fact that they have the gene (or gene pair) that in a majority of instances "causes" the trait. In such cases the trait (or the gene) is said to be nonpenetrant. Penetrance is an all-or-none proposition. Nonpenetrance occurs at the mild end of the curve of expressivity. One may think of the manifestation curve of the mutant gene as overlapping at the mild end with the expressivity curve in "normals," or at least in those who do not carry the gene that is being studied (Fig. 4.1). In the area of overlap the persons with the gene cannot be distinguished from those without the gene. The threshold of penetrance, represented by a vertical line cutting the expressivity curve, moves progressively to the left as methods for analyzing the phenotype become more discerning. Penetrance and nonpenetrance are often functions of the acuteness of our methods of study. Figure 4.2 gives an example of the overlap of phenotypes when individual effects of a single gene pair, in this case that

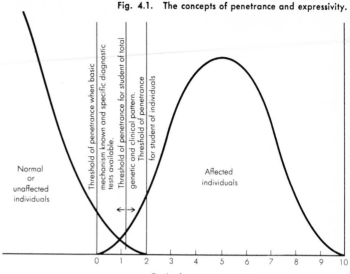

Fig. 4.1.   The concepts of penetrance and expressivity.

Threshold of penetrance when basic mechanism known and specific diagnostic tests available.

Threshold of penetrance for student of total genetic and clinical pattern.

Threshold of penetrance for student of individuals

Normal
or
unaffected
individuals

Affected
individuals

0   1   2   3   4   5   6   7   8   9   10

Grade of severity (expressivity)

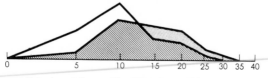

0   5   10   15   20   30   40

Phenylalanine in blood plasma (mg. %)

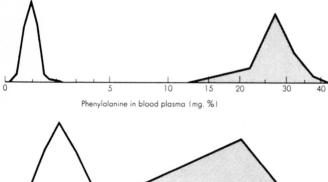

150   100   50   20   0

Intelligence (Binet, I.Q.)

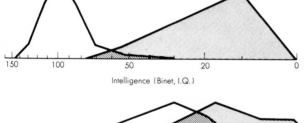

350   330   310   290   270

Head size.   Length + breadth in mm. (corrected for sex)

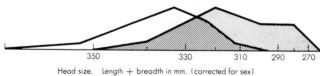

0   5   10   15   20   25   30   35   40

Hair color.   Reflectance % at 700 mμ (corrected for age)

Fig. 4.2. Frequency distributions of some characteristics of phenylketonuria in · phenylketonuric patients (shaded) and in control populations. Hair color and head size show pronounced overlap, and intelligence shows some overlap. The level of phenylalanine in the blood, however, is higher in all phenylketonurics than in controls. If intelligence were the only phenotype used in the analysis, the genotype would be said to be nonpenetrant in a small proportion of cases. When plasma level of phenylalanine is the phenotype, the genotype is found to be fully penetrant. Redrawn from Penrose, *Ann. Eugenics,* **16** (1951), 134.

for phenylketonuria, are singled out for analysis. If hair color, head size, and intelligence were the only phenotypic characteristics available for distinguishing phenylketonuric patients from normals, the error in diagnosis would be considerable. The genotype could be said to be nonpenetrant in a great number of persons. But when the level of phenylalanine in the, blood is used as the phenotype for study, the genotype is fully penetrant.

In medicine many hereditary disorders are syndromes. Meaning literally "a running together," this word refers to combinations of manifestations that occur together with reasonable consistency. Most genetic syndromes have their basis in a single mutant gene. The manifold features are often the consequence of the fact that the mutant gene and its wild-type counterpart have a widespread role in the body's economy. Or the effects of the mutant gene may be such that a substance toxic to several different tissues accumulates in the body. There are other mechanisms for multiple and often seemingly distinct manifestations of a single gene. At the phenotypic level, it is permissible to refer to the gene as *pleiotropic* (pronounced ply-o-tropic) in its action, that is, having multiple effects. *Polyphenic* is also a good term for describing the gene responsible for such syndromes, but one must remember that at the level of primary gene action there is no evidence that one gene has more than one function.

As far as is known, the association of traits in no heritable syndrome of man is the result of close linkage of several genes, each responsible for one of the aspects of the syndrome. That several linked genes would mutate simultaneously to reproduce a given syndrome with exactitude is unlikely. If all instances of the syndrome were the result of a unique event in the remote past, then the several genes would be likely to have become separated through the process of crossing over and no particular association of the several manifestations would be observable.

It is true that a genetic syndrome like Down's syndrome (Mongoloid idiocy) has a basis other than in a single gene. Presumably dosage effect of many genes carried on chromosome 21 and present in excess is responsible for the characteristic clinical picture of trisomy 21 (see p. 18). It is possible, furthermore, that certain very rare syndromes that are transmitted in a Mendelian manner are the result of small chromosomal aberrations, such as deletion or inversion, affecting the action of several genes.

Genetics: the study of variation

Environmental factors in variation are of secondary interest to the geneticist but can never be disregarded. Discontinuous variation, such that persons can be classified as having a given trait or not having the trait, is more easily studied, especially in man, than is continuous variation. Consequently, the amount of precise genetic information is greater for discontinuous traits than it is for continuous traits.

Professor E. B. Ford of Oxford has described polymorphic traits in a famous definition that is quoted like a verse of scripture: "*Polymorphism* may be defined as the occurrence together in the same habitat of two or more discontinuous forms of a species in such proportions that the rarest of them cannot be maintained merely by recurrent mutation." The definition is so worded that geographic differences and those due to rare disease alleles constantly eliminated by natural selection and replaced by mutation are not included in the category of polymorphisms.

In man polymorphism has been demonstrated by a variety of methods for studying the phenotype:

(1) Physiologic methods. Color blindness satisfies Ford's definition. So does PTC-tasting—the ability or lack of ability to taste phenylthiocarbamide—although no complete separation between taster and nontaster groups is achieved.

(2) Morphologic methods. One has difficulty citing a morphologic trait that is relatively frequent and at the same time is a clearly "discontinuous form." Red hair and blue eyes tend to segregate as autosomal recessive characters. However, hair and eye color, attached or unattached ear lobes, clockwise or counterclockwise "cowlick" (hair whorl), etc., have some features of continuous characters and are not readily amenable to simple Mendelian interpretation.

(3) Electrophoretic methods. Various types of electrophoresis—e.g., on paper and in starch gel—have been used to demonstrate polymorphism of hemoglobin and of serum proteins (e.g., the haptoglobins and transferrins). See Fig. 4.13 for a demonstration of haptoglobin types.

(4) Immunologic methods. The red blood cell groups ("blood groups"), starting with the ABO system discovered by Landsteiner in 1900, represent the outstanding examples of immunologically demonstrated polymorphism. The gamma globulin groups (Gm) of human serum are also demonstrated by immunologic techniques.

(5) Immunoelectrophoretic methods, a combination of the last two, have been used to demonstrate polymorphism of the α_2 globulins of serum (the Gc types) and of beta lipoproteins (the Ag types).

(6) Metabolic methods, which might be included in the category of physiologic methods, have been used to demonstrate polymorphism with regard to the rate of acetylation of isoniazid, a drug used in the treatment of tuberculosis.

(7) Enzymatic methods demonstrate differences in red cell glucose-

6-phosphate dehydrogenase. Deficiency of this enzyme, an X-linked trait, occurs as a polymorphism in African and Mediterranean populations.

New techniques for demonstrating discontinuous variation in man are much to be desired. Simple observational methods have limited usefulness. Few genetic markers for linkage studies—discontinuous traits with impeccable Mendelian transmission—are available. All science is enslaved to its methods. By his invention of starch gel electrophoresis, Oliver Smithies contributed greatly to human genetics as well as to protein chemistry. A number of genetic polymorphisms, for example, that of the haptoglobins, have been demonstrated with this technique.

Protein structure and gene action

Earlier it was stated that one gene has one function. There is now good evidence that for many genes (so-called "structural" genes) the function is to specify the amino acid sequence of a protein or of one polypeptide chain. The protein so specified may be an enzyme; it may be a protein, such as hemoglobin or haptoglobin, with a special function; or it may be a structural protein such as collagen. Much of the present knowledge of gene action, especially the role of the gene in protein synthesis, is based on study of the sickle-cell condition, a polymorphism of man. Because this important area is discussed in full in another book of this series (*Gene Action*) only a résumé will be provided here.

The history of the development of knowledge of sickle hemoglobin illustrates the various levels of sophistication in the analysis of phenotype. First, sickling (a peculiar shape of the red blood cell) and sickle-cell anemia were identified (Fig. 4.3a). From family studies, it was concluded that those persons in whom only sickling occurred were heterozygous, whereas persons in whom severe anemia accompanied sickling were homozygous. Then, Linus Pauling and his colleagues discovered that the hemoglobin in sickle-cell anemia patients has an electrophoretic mobility different from the hemoglobin of normal persons (Fig. 4.3b) and that the hemoglobin of heterozygotes is partly of the normal type (hemoglobin A) and partly of the sickle type (sickle hemoglobin, or Hb S).

Thereafter it was found that the normal hemoglobin molecule is a tetramer, that is, is made up of four polypeptide chains: two identical alpha chains and two identical beta chains (Fig. 4.4). The peculiarity of sickle hemoglobin is a feature of the beta chains. The alpha chains of Hb S are identical to those of Hb A.

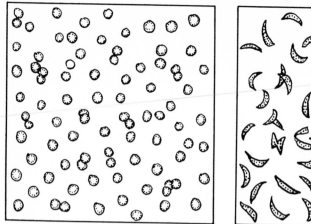
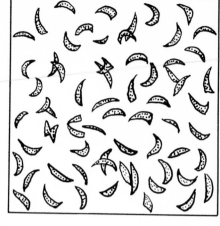

a

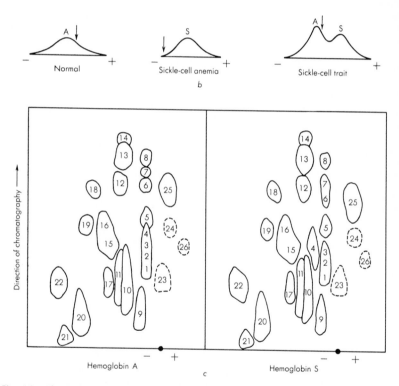

A ↓

Normal

↓ S

Sickle-cell anemia

A ↓ S

Sickle-cell trait

b

Direction of chromatography →

Hemoglobin A

− +

Hemoglobin S

− +

c

Fig. 4.3. Phenotypes produced by sickle hemoglobin (Hb S). (*a*) A comparison of "sickled" erythrocytes with normal ones. (*b*) Paper electrophoresis of the hemoglobin of a normal subject, homozygous AA; a person with sickle-cell anemia, homozygous SS; and one with sickle-cell trait, heterozygous SA. (*c*) "Fingerprint" of hemoglobin A and hemoglobin S.

Next it was demonstrated that the defect in sickle hemoglobin is limited to one peptide of the β-polypeptide chain (Fig. 4.4). Vernon Ingram applied to hemoglobin the technique of fingerprinting. In this

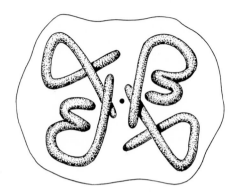

Fig. 4.4. A schematic representation of the two alpha and two beta chains of the hemoglobin molecule. After Ingram, *Nature, 184* (1959), 1905.

technique the polypeptide chains are broken up into peptide fragments by means of the enzyme trypsin. The mixture of peptides is then spread out on paper by electrophoresis followed by chromatography at right angles to the direction of the electrophoresis. The resulting display of the peptides is the fingerprint (Fig. 4.3c). The results of this method show that sickle hemoglobin differs from the normal with respect to one peptide.

When the amino acid sequence of the aberrant peptide was compared with that of the normal peptide that it replaced, the following was found.

Hb A   valine-histidine-leucine-threonine-proline-
        glutamic acid-glutamic acid-lysine-

Hb S   valine-histidine-leucine-threonine-proline-
        valine-glutamic acid-lysine-

It is now known that the segment of the beta chain shown above is at the nitrogen ($-NH_2$) end and that the beta chain contains 146 amino acids, only one of which in sickle hemoglobin is different from the normal. The reason Hb S is slower in its electrophoretic mobility is that it is lacking the negative charge of the glutamic acid residue in Hb A; valine, unlike glutamic acid, has no free charge.

Several other variant hemoglobins have been found to have an amino acid change in the beta chain. In one of these, hemoglobin C, the very same amino acid is involved: lysine is substituted for glutamic acid as the sixth amino acid in the beta chain. All of the variant hemoglobins with changes in the beta chain appear to be determined by genes allelic with each other (see p. 45).

Other variant hemoglobins, e.g., Hb Hopkins-2, so-called because it was a second variant discovered at the Johns Hopkins Hospital, show a change in the alpha chain. On the basis of families in which both an alpha-chain mutation and a beta-chain mutation are segregating it has been concluded that the mutations are nonallelic; that is, that separate genetic loci determine the alpha and beta chains. The loci may even be on separate chromosomes.

The concept currently accepted is that genes act by determining the amino acid sequence of proteins, or rather, as the hemoglobin evidence shows us, polypeptide chains. This formulation is a logical outgrowth of Beadle and Tatum's one-gene–one-enzyme hypothesis of 1940. Clearly their hypothesis was too restrictive since the protein specified is not necessarily an enzyme; "one-gene–one-polypeptide" is a better statement of what is currently thought to be the case. The genetic locus is thought of as the unit that specifies the amino acid sequence of one polypeptide. The cistron, or functional unit, of Seymour Benzer can be considered synonymous; i.e., it has the same physical limits as the locus. Sites (or codons) are the subunits of the locus, each encoding the information for one amino acid. Presumably the mutations in Hb S and Hb C are at the same site. The mutations responsible for Hb E and other beta-chain-variant hemoglobins are at the same locus but not at the same site. Recombination can occur within the locus so that the recon, or recombination unit, of Benzer is something less than the locus. It is theoretically possible, for example, that a child with only Hb A or a child with a hemoglobin containing two amino acid substitutions might occur among the children of an individual with both Hb S and Hb E, married to a person with only Hb A. Since the probability of crossing over, which could produce such a result, is directly related to the distance separating the reference points, crossing over between two sites as close as those involved in Hb S and Hb E would be very rare.

The muton (mutational unit) and recon (recombination unit), in the terminology of Benzer, are indeed even smaller than the site. Assuming a triplet code for each amino acid, one can see that a change in only one base would represent a mutation. Furthermore, recombination can occur between two bases.

Information from studies of the genetic code in cell-free systems correlates well with information on the change in certain aberrant hemoglobins. The RNA code word for glutamic acid is UAG. The mutation responsible for Hb S and Hb C is a change in a single base, because the code word for valine is UUG and that for lysine is UAA. (U = uridine; A = adenine; G = guanine. In the DNA code thymine replaces uridine.) In the above code words, e.g., UAG, the order of the letters as given is not necessarily the correct one.

The genetic control of hemoglobin synthesis is more complicated than what has been presented so far. During fetal life man has a different hemoglobin, in which the alpha chains are chemically identical to those of adult Hb A, and evidence indicates that they have the same genetic control; however, in place of the beta chain, fetal hemoglobin contains a chemically different gamma chain that is under the control of a separate genetic locus.

In the normal adult there is, moreover, a minor hemoglobin component called Hb A_2, that again has alpha chains that are identical chemically and genetically to those of Hb A, Hb S, and Hb F; yet another type of polypeptide chain, called the delta chain, is substituted for the beta chain.

Just as one writes the formula of water H_2O, one can write the formulas of these hemoglobins as follows:

$$Hb\ A \quad = \alpha_2^A \beta_2^A$$
$$Hb\ F \quad = \alpha_2^A \gamma_2^F$$
$$Hb\ A_2 \quad = \alpha_2^A \delta_2^{A_2}$$
$$Hb\ S \quad = \alpha_2^A \beta_2^S$$
$$Hb\ C \quad = \alpha_2^A \beta_2^C$$
$$Hb\ Ho\text{-}2 = \alpha_2^{Ho\text{-}2} \beta_2^A$$

(Hopkins-2)

Even more specific chemical formulas for the hemoglobins stating the specific amino acid change are possible on the basis of information from fingerprinting and related analyses: e.g.,

$$Hb\ S = \alpha_2^A \beta_2^{6\ Val}$$
$$Hb\ C = \alpha_2^A \beta_2^{6\ Lys}$$

Up to this point, four separate loci that control the synthesis of hemoglobin have been described: (1) The alpha locus controlling synthesis of dimers of α-polypeptide chains and active throughout life, both intrauterine and postnatal; (2) the beta locus controlling the synthesis of dimers of β-polypeptide chains and active mainly in postnatal life; (3) the gamma locus controlling the synthesis of dimers of γ-polypeptide chains and active mainly in fetal life; and (4) the delta locus controlling the synthesis of δ-polypeptide chains and active mainly in postnatal life. The beta, gamma, and delta dimers are each capable of combining with alpha dimers to form separate species of protein: Hb A, Hb F, and Hb A_2, respectively. Figure 4.5 summarizes this scheme of the genetic control of hemoglobin synthesis. Figure 4.6 presents the explanation of the findings when the individual is heterozygous at two of these loci.

The study of the genetics of hemoglobin synthesis and related subjects has shown that the gene (at least many genes called "structural" genes) determines the amino acid sequence, or primary structure, of a polypeptide chain; that the secondary (helical) and tertiary (folding) structures and the physical and functional properties of the polypeptide are a consequence of its primary structure; and that more than one species of polypeptide chain, each with separate genetic control, may be combined in a single protein. (Three or four other proteins in man are known to be composed of two or more distinct polypeptide chains

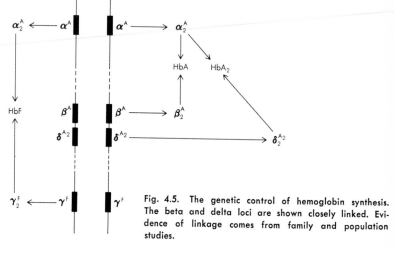

Fig. 4.5. The genetic control of hemoglobin synthesis. The beta and delta loci are shown closely linked. Evidence of linkage comes from family and population studies.

Fig. 4.6. Multiple hemoglobins. Persons heterozygous at both the alpha locus and the beta locus have four types of major hemoglobin. In this example the individual is doubly heterozygous for Hb S and Hb Hopkins-2. (See page 45 and Fig. 3.12). In addition (not diagrammed here) such a person has two types of minor hemoglobin, A_2 and A_2^{Ho-2}, and in fetal life two types of fetal hemoglobin, $\alpha_2^{A}\gamma^{F}$ and $\alpha_2^{Ho-2}\gamma^{F}$. Based on Baglioni, in Taylor, ed., *Molecular Genetics* (Academic, 1963).

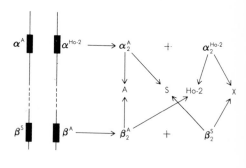

under separate genetic control.) These studies have clarified the concepts of the nature of the mutational, recombinational, and functional units of genetic material in man.

Control mechanisms in gene action

Some genes have a controlling role rather than a role in determining the amino acid sequence of proteins. A possible example in man is provided again by studies of the genetics of hemoglobin synthesis. A "switch" gene seems to be involved in the change from synthesis of gamma chains (Hb F) in fetal life to the synthesis of beta chains (Hb A) in postnatal life. Persons have been found, however, with high Hb F in adult life. Incidentally, this has no apparent ill effects, even in persons who are homozygous for this mutation and have only Hb F. The regulation by the "switch" gene must be at the level of the chromosome because the person heterozygous for the "high-F" gene has about half Hb F and half Hb A. Furthermore, the person heterozygous (in repulsion) for both the high-F gene and the sickle gene has no Hb A but shows no interference with Hb S synthesis.

The homozygote for high F not only has no Hb A but also has none of the minor component normally found in the adult, Hb A_2 ($\alpha_2{}^A\delta_2{}^{A_2}$). The delta locus (locus for δ-polypeptide chains) is closely linked with the beta locus (p. 53). Thus, a plausible model envisions an "operator" gene that controls the function of at least two structural genes, the beta locus and the delta locus (Fig. 4.7). The postulated operator gene and the beta and delta structural genes, and possibly the gamma gene as well, constitute a unit of the type François Jacob and Jacques Monod have called the *operon*. In addition, there may be one or more regulator loci in other chromosomes that influence the function of individual structural genes.

Garrodian inborn errors of metabolism

Up to this point, the proteins that have been considered as products of gene action are not enzymes. Hemoglobin, not an enzyme in the strict sense, has an important function in oxygen transport.

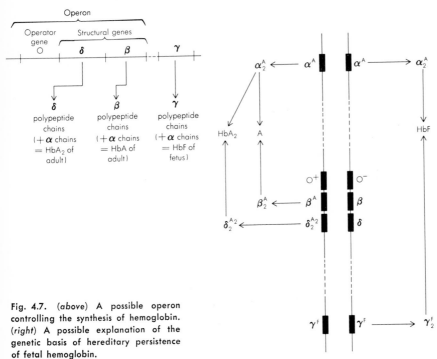

Fig. 4.7. (*above*) A possible operon controlling the synthesis of hemoglobin. (*right*) A possible explanation of the genetic basis of hereditary persistence of fetal hemoglobin.

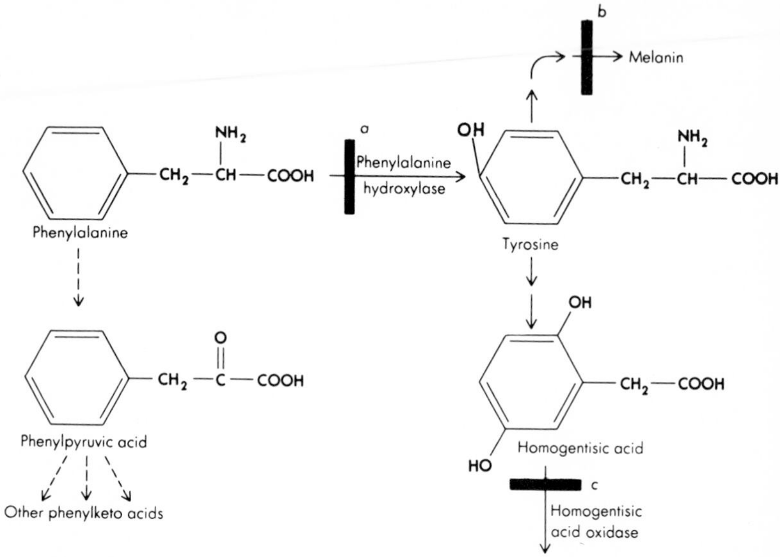

Fig. 4.8.   The site of the enzyme defect in four disorders of aromatic amino acid metabolism. The heavy bars indicate the block in (a) phenylketonuria, (b) albinism, and (c) alkaptonuria. The solid arrows indicate reactions important in normal metabolism. The broken arrows indicate reactions that become important in phenylketonuria.

The haptoglobins, transferrins, and gamma globulins are nonenzymatic serum proteins whose functions are at least partly understood. But some of the proteins specified by genes are enzymes. A mutation in the gene that determines a given enzyme may produce a disorder of the type Garrod called inborn errors of metabolism. Much has been learned about the genetic control of enzymes and about intermediary metabolism by a study of mutant forms in the human species as well as in microorganisms.

Alkaptonuria is a useful model for discussion of inborn errors of metabolism and has historical precedence, since it was the condition that was the basis for Garrod's concepts. The defect involves homogentisic acid oxidase (homogentisicase), an enzyme that is involved in the metabolism of homogentisic acid (see Fig. 4.8c). Large amounts of homogentisic acid are excreted in the urine and turn black in alkaline urine or upon exposure to light. The black urine, causing, for example, staining of the diapers, calls attention to the condition. In addition, aggregates of homogentisic acid accumulate in the body, and become attached to the collagen of cartilage and other connective tissues. The cartilage of the ears and the sclera, which is collagenous in nature, is stained black. These manifestations are called *ochronosis*. In the joints, such as those of the spine, the accumulations lead to arthritis.

Alkaptonuria is an example of a genetic enzyme block in which the phenotypic features are caused by the accumulation of excess substances just proximal to the block (Fig. 4.9b).

In some other genetic blocks in intermediary metabolism the phenotypic consequences are related to the lack of a normal product distal to the block (Fig. 4.9c). An example is albinism in which the genetic block involves a step between the amino acid tyrosine and the pigment melanin (Fig. 4.8b).

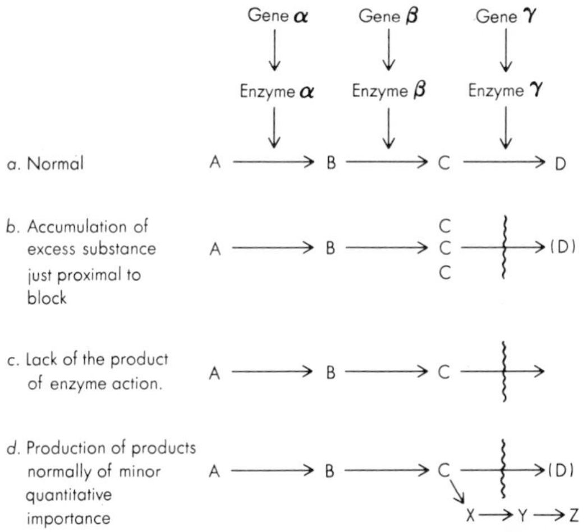

Gene α   Gene β   Gene γ

Enzyme α   Enzyme β   Enzyme γ

a. Normal   A ⟶ B ⟶ C ⟶ D

b. Accumulation of excess substance just proximal to block   A ⟶ B ⟶ C / C / C ⟶ (D)

Fig. 4.9. Schematic representation of three of the ways in which a genetically determined enzyme block can produce phenotypic abnormalities: (a) the normal situation; (b) the situation in alkaptonuria; (c) in albinism; (d) in phenylketonuria.

c. Lack of the product of enzyme action.   A ⟶ B ⟶ C ⟶

d. Production of products normally of minor quantitative importance   A ⟶ B ⟶ C ⟶ (D); X ⟶ Y ⟶ Z

In other inborn errors of metabolism the phenotypic consequences result from excessive production of a product of what is normally an alternative and minor metabolic pathway (Fig. 4.9d). Phenylketonuria, like alkaptonuria and albinism, is a genetic defect in aromatic amino acid metabolism (see Fig. 4.8a). The defect is in the enzyme involved in the conversion of phenylalanine to tyrosine. The affected person has lighter pigmentation than normal, but is not a complete albino since tyrosine is available in the diet. Severe mental retardation, one of the most prominent symptoms, is probably the result of untoward effects on brain metabolism of certain metabolic products of phenylalanine formed through alternative pathways. Certain of these alternative metabolites of phenylalanine, especially phenylpyruvic acid, are excreted in the urine and are one basis for diagnosis of the disorder. The difference in phenotype of these three diseases—alkaptonuria, phenylketonuria, and albinism—despite the fact that they involve closely related metabolic steps, is noteworthy.

Essentially all inborn errors of metabolism are inherited as recessives; the clinical disorder is present only in the homozygote. The heterozygote does not manifest the disorder; apparently a double dose of enzyme is no better than a single dose under usual circumstances. In several conditions, however, the heterozygous carrier can be identified by special means, one of which involves stressing the particular enzymatic step. In phenylketonuria, for example, the phenotypically normal but genetically heterozygous parents of affected persons tend to show blood levels of phenylalanine that are higher and last longer than normal when a standard dose of this amino acid is administered. This is the so-called phenylalanine tolerance test (Fig. 4.10).

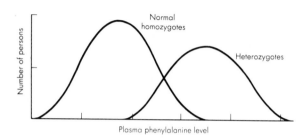

Fig. 4.10. The phenylalanine tolerance test in the heterozygous parents of patients with phenylketonuria.

A second method for demonstrating the heterozygote is illustrated by galactosemia. In this disorder absence of the enzyme galactose-1-phosphate uridyl transferase renders the homozygote incapable of metabolizing galactose of milk. The enzyme defect can conveniently be demonstrated in the circulating red blood cells. The heterozygote tends to have an enzyme level intermediate between that of the two homozygotes, the normal and the affected (Fig. 4.11).

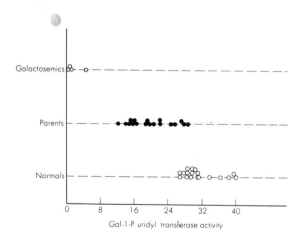

Fig. 4.11. Level of galactose-1-phosphate uridyl transferase in the erythrocytes of normals, of homozygous galactosemic subjects, and of heterozygous parents of galactosemic infants. Redrawn from Kirkman and Bynum, *Ann. Human Genet.*, 23 (1959), 117.

Defects in active transport mechanisms

Garrod investigated four conditions he considered inborn errors of metabolism: alkaptonuria, albinism, cystinuria, and pentosuria. It is now known that one of these, cystinuria, is not really an inborn error of metabolism. Large amounts of cystine appear in the urine not because of a defect in intermediary metabolism but rather because of a defect in the renal tubule mechanism by which cystine is resorbed from the glomerular filtrate. Normal resorption is accomplished by an active transport mechanism; that is, a metabolic process is involved in transferring cystine and other amino acids from the lumen of the renal tubule (where it has arrived by filtration through the glomerulus) to the blood stream on the other side of the renal tubule cell. At the molecular level the distinction between genetic defects in active transport systems and inborn errors of metabolism is probably artificial; enzyme defects may be involved in both. Other genetic defects in active transport mechanisms have been discovered.

Dosage effect

In a number of instances in which it is possible to measure the primary product of gene action, one finds that the heterozygote has about half as much of the product as does the homozygote. The example of gal-1-P uridyl transferase in galactosemia heterozygote has already been cited in Fig. 4.11. Sometimes the heterozygote does not have exactly half as much product protein as the homozygote. For example, the sickling heterozygote, SA, has normal levels of total hemoglobin, but Hb A represents about 70 per cent rather than 50 per cent of the total. (This is evident in Fig. 4.3.) The reason for the inequality is currently under study.

Dosage effect in connection with X-linked genes

For genes on the X chromosome a special problem of dosage effect exists, and the following questions arise: Does the female with two X chromosomes have twice as much gene product, such as the enzyme glucose-6-phosphate dehydrogenase or the blood-clotting factor antihemophilic globulin, as does the male with one X chromosome? If a dosage effect of the two X chromosomes is not observed in the normal female, what is the mechanism of dosage compensation?

One could imagine that to avoid disruptive dosage effects the X chromosome might have been largely stripped of genetic information in evolution. That this is not the case, however, is indicated by the considerable list of traits known to be determined by genes on the X chromosome. The X chromosome seems to carry at least as much genetic information as an autosome of comparable length. Furthermore, studies suggest that the normal male and normal female have essentially identical amounts of gene product for a number of traits determined by genes on the X chromosome.

A possible mechanism of dosage compensation in X-linked traits was mentioned earlier in connection with serum albumin and the condition analbuminemia. Through feedback inhibition a given gene might have the same effects whether present in single dose in the hemizygous male or in double dose in the female. In fact, however, a number of X-linked traits have been studied in which the heterozygous female shows an intermediate level of the gene product.

The Lyon hypothesis (Fig. 4.12) provides an explanation for both dosage compensation and the findings in heterozygous females. As outlined earlier (p. 18), the explanation that occurred to Dr. Mary Lyon

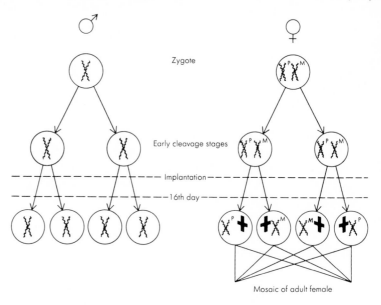

Fig. 4.12. A schematic representation of the Lyon hypothesis.

of Harwell, England, and simultaneously to several other workers, is that after a time early in embryogenesis one X chromosome becomes genetically inactive and forms the Barr body of interphase nuclei (p. 17). The Lyon hypothesis further suggests (1) that it is a random matter as to which X chromosome in any single cell—whether the one derived from the father or the one from the mother—is the inactive one, and (2) that once the differentiation of the X chromosome, one assuming an inactive role, has occurred in a given cell, then the *same* X chromosome remains inactive in all descendants of that cell. The primordial germ cells of the female, even though they have two X chromosomes, do not participate in this process of X-chromosome differentiation.

The Lyon hypothesis provides a mechanism for dosage compensation since the female has no more *active* X chromosomes than does the male. The Lyon hypothesis is obviously not in conflict with the facts of X-linked recessive inheritance. In the hemizygous male whose X chromosome carries, for example, the mutant "gene for hemophilia," every gene in his body at the locus for antihemophilic globulin (which is deficient in hemophilia) is of the mutant type. In the heterozygous female who carries the hemophilia gene on one X chromosome and the wild-type allele on the other X chromosome, half the antihemophilic-globulin genes, on the average, are of the mutant type and half are wild type, if there is an equal probability that the mutant X chromosome will be the active or the inactive one in any given body cell.

The Lyon hypothesis also provides an explanation for the intermediate level of gene product in the heterozygous female and for the rather wide variability in the level of gene product observed in heterozygotes of several X-linked disorders. Since the decision as to which X chromosome will be the inactive one is made early in embryogenesis, the number of cells is relatively small. Especially small is the number of pertinent anlage cells destined for a particular function, let us say, synthesis of antihemophilic globulin; perhaps only about a dozen such cells are present at the "time of decision." By chance alone, rare individuals might have all cells with the mutant X chromosome as the active one; such individuals would be hemophilic—so-called "manifesting heterozygotes." Or all cells might by chance have the wild-type X chromosome active; these individuals would have normal levels of antihemophilic globulin. But the great majority of heterozygous females would have an intermediate proportion of cells with the mutant X chromosome active.

If the Lyon hypothesis is valid and all cells in a particular line have the same X chromosome inactive, one would anticipate that the heterozygous female would display mosaicism for those X-linked traits in which the phenotype is evident at the cellular level. Mosaicism of the predicted type has been demonstrated for several conditions in heterozygotes; notable among the examples is glucose-6-phosphate dehydrogenase deficiency. Heterozygous females have been shown to have two populations of cells, those with normal enzyme activity and those with very little enzyme activity.

Although the Lyon hypothesis cannot be considered completely proved, the evidence to date suggests that it is substantially correct and that dosage compensation for X-borne genes is determined mainly by this mechanism.

Gene interaction

Gene interaction is observed between alleles and between non-alleles. Allelic interaction is well illustrated by the example of haptoglobin, a serum protein that shows genetic variation (Fig. 4.13). Two alleles that occur frequently have been recognized—Hp^1 (hapto-

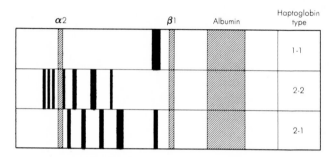

Fig. 4.13. The haptoglobins (in black) as demonstrated by starch gel electrophoresis—a schematic representation. The cross-hatched areas represent other proteins. Redrawn from Giblett and Steinberg, Am. J. Human Genet., 12 (1960), 160.

globin-1) and Hp^2 (haptoglobin-2). The haptoglobin types of the two homozygotes are referred to as Hp 1-1 and Hp 2-2. In the heterozygote the haptoglobin is not a mixture of Hp 1-1 and Hp 2-2 proteins; instead the heterozygote has a unique protein product with chemical properties quite distinct from those of the proteins produced by the two homozygotes. It has been suggested that some instances of heterozygote advantage might have a basis in the formation of a unique protein by the heterozygote through gene interaction.

Nonallelic interaction is illustrated by several phenomena associated with blood groups, and is best understood by a discussion of them.

Blood groups

The blood groups share with the hemoglobins the distinction of having contributed heavily to the formulation of principles of human genetics and of genetics in general. Blood groups are, furthermore, of great significance in medicine. It would be well for the student to become acquainted with a few basic facts about the blood groups and to understand their importance to human genetics and to medicine.

The blood groups are genetically determined antigens of the red blood cells. At least 12 different blood-group systems, each determined by a separate locus, have been identified. Furthermore, at most of these separate loci multiple alleles are now known.

The different antigens on the red cells are identified by means of antibodies—proteins in serum that combine with the antigens and produce such effects as agglutination of the red cells. Some of the antibodies occur naturally; for example, in the ABO blood-group system, type A persons have in their serum antibody against type B cells; type B persons have antibody against type A cells; and type O persons have antibody against both type A and type B cells. Consequently Landsteiner was able to demonstrate the ABO blood types by mixing the serum and red cells of different persons.

To demonstrate the antigens of other blood groups, it is necessary to obtain the corresponding antibody by one of two methods. In the case of the MN blood groups the antibody was produced in another species, the rabbit, by injecting human red blood cells into it. Rabbits injected with cells from persons of the *MM* genotype produced anti-*M* serum; cells from persons of the *NN* genotype stimulated production of anti-*N* serum. Cells from persons of the *MN* genotype, i.e., heterozygotes, were agglutinated by either anti-*M* or anti-*N* rabbit serum.

The other method by which antibodies demonstrating blood groups are developed is the accidental development of antibody by a pregnant woman or a transfused patient. If the mother lacks a red cell antigen that is present in the fetus (who inherited it from the father), the mother may develop antibodies against the antigen when fetal cells leak over into the mother. The Rh blood types, as well as several of the others, were discovered largely through this mechanism. A situation that in principle is exactly the same occurs when a patient, transfused with red cells containing an antigen he does not possess, develops a serum antibody against that antigen. The X-linked blood group Xg^a was discovered in this way.

Blood groups are of great genetic significance; they provided some of the clearest early examples of simple Mendelian inheritance. The blood groups are co-dominant. In many instances—in fact so often that it is now considered a general principle—an antibody is eventually discovered for both antigens present in the heterozygote. Thus, in the Kell system an antiserum was first discovered that agglutinated the red cells from persons of the genotype *KK* or *Kk* but not of persons of genotype *kk*. Later an antiserum was found that agglutinated the red cells from persons of the genotype *Kk* or *kk*.

The Hardy-Weinberg principle (p. 112) was first put to test in connection with the ABO blood groups. Multiple allelism was first demonstrated in man in the case of the ABO types. In fact, Bernstein proved multiple allelism (rather than two loci, one determining A and non-A and the other B and non-B) by showing that the phenotype frequencies agree with those predicted by the Hardy–Weinberg principle for a multiple allele system.

Most of the markers useful for genetic linkage studies are blood groups. Population genetics has made extensive use of the blood groups; the influence of selection, drift, and gene flow has been studied on the basis of blood groups. Blood groups also illustrate the difficulties in distinguishing close linkage and allelism in man. A transatlantic polemic raged over this matter in regard to the Rh blood-group system. Sir Ronald Fisher and Robert R. Race in England suggested that three closely linked loci were responsible for the Rh specificities that they termed C, D, and E. Alexander Wiener in this country insisted that a single complex locus was involved. Current thinking favors Wiener's interpretation.

The secretor and ABO loci show nonallelic interaction. The secretor trait is characterized by the secretion of ABO blood group antigen in the saliva. About 70 per cent of persons of northern European origin are secretors. But to secrete type A antigen the person must be both of genotypes AA, AB, or AO and of genotype SS or Ss. Imagine that nothing was known of red cell blood types and that the only phenotype that could be tested was the presence or absence of A antigen in the saliva. The distribution of these phenotypes in families and in populations would be quite different from that of phenotypes dependent on a single gene difference.

Suppression is illustrated by the rare Bombay phenomenon—so called because it was first detected in a family in India. Persons were found who were of blood group O but who, from the blood types of

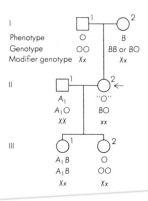

Fig. 4.14. The Bombay phenomenon. After Levine *et al., Blood,* 10 (1955), 1100.

their parents and children (Fig. 4.14), were known to carry the gene for blood type B (or A). The explanation assigned to the findings was that these individuals are homozygous for a rare recessive suppressor gene (xx), or viewed differently, for a mutation in a gene essential to the development of the ABO blood-group antigen. In the absence of at least one dominant X gene a precursor substance may not be formed.

The importance of blood groups to medicine lies in at least three areas. (1) Uncomplicated blood transfusion requires recognition and understanding of these genetic differences. (2) The proper management and prevention of the ill-effects of materno-fetal incompatibility (e.g., Rh problems of pregnancy) likewise must be based on a clear understanding of blood group principles. (3) Medico-legal applications include cases of disputed parentage. Usually there is no question about the identity of the mother and only paternity is in doubt. Paternity can never be proved with absolute certainty but can be disproved in two ways: (a) A man is excluded as the father if he and the mother both lack an antigen that the child possesses. The child cannot have an antigen lacking in both parents—barring rare phenomena such as the Bombay trait and mutation. (b) A man is excluded if the child fails to show an antigen he must transmit. For example, an AB man cannot have an O child, nor can an M man have an N child.

References

Baglioni, Corrado, "Correlations Between Genetics and Chemistry of Human Hemoglobins," in *Molecular Genetics*, Vol. I, J. H. Taylor, ed. New York: Academic Press, Inc., 1963, pp. 405-75.

Garrod, Archibald E., *Inborn Errors of Metabolism*. Reprinted with a supplement by Harry Harris. London: Oxford University Press, 1963.

Ingram, Vernon M., *Hemoglobins in Genetics and Evolution*. New York: Columbia University Press, 1963.

Race, Robert R., and Ruth Sanger, *Blood Groups in Man*, 4th ed. Oxford: Blackwell Scientific Publications, 1962.

Stanbury, J. B., J. B. Wyngaarten, and D. S. Fredrickson, eds., *The Metabolic Basis of Inherited Disease*. New York: McGraw-Hill Book Company, 1960. A comprehensive survey of inborn errors of metabolism.

$\mathcal{F}ive$

Genes in Development
and Differentiation

The central question of embryogenesis and differentiation is why certain genes function only at certain times and in certain tissues. All somatic cells contain the same complement of genes, yet only erythroblasts synthesize hemoglobin and only liver cells synthesize serum albumin, to cite two examples.

Hemoglobin provides a particularly clear example in man of the function of one gene in fetal life and another in extrauterine life. The genetic locus responsible for production of α-polypeptide chains of hemoglobin is functional throughout the life of the organism, beginning at a relatively early stage of embryogenesis. However, the separate genetic locus determining production of β-polypeptide chains of hemoglobin is quiescent in fetal life, when a third genetic locus is active and determines the production of γ-polypeptide chains that combine with α-polypeptide chains to form fetal hemoglobin. At about the time of birth the gamma locus is "turned off" and the beta locus is "turned on." An operator gene (Fig. 4.7) appears to be involved in turning on the beta locus, but the problem is only moved back one step to the question of what controls the operator gene.

Studies of the enzyme lactic acid dehydrogenase provide evidence of differences in genic activity in different tissues. This enzyme protein is a tetramer consisting of four polypeptide chains. The chains can be of two different types, A and B. Five different proteins are formed depending on the proportions of A and B chains: A_4, A_3B_1, A_2B_2, A_1B_4, and B_4, the last having most rapid electrophoretic migration. (These are sometimes referred to as LDH 5, 4, 3, 2, and 1, respectively.) Each of these five proteins has characteristic physical and enzymatic properties, and which ones of the five proteins are present in a given tissue is a characteristic of that tissue at a particular stage of development. During development the proportions of the five enzymes change in many tissues. For example, all human embryonic tissues have predominantly B_4 (LDH 1), as does adult heart muscle, but adult skeletal muscle has predominantly A_4 (LDH 5). The A and B chains are apparently under separate genetic control; a mutation involving each has been found in man. The relative activity of these genes determines which of the five enzymes predominate in a given cell at a given stage.

Intrauterine selection is undoubtedly rigorous, even under the presently improved conditions of prenatal care in civilized countries. It is estimated that 15 to 25 per cent of zygotes are lost before birth. Many of these may have gross chromosomal aberrations, such as triploidy, which has been identified in some abortions. Others probably have more subtle defects. Materno-fetal incompatibility for the ABO blood groups is known to lead to early fetal death and abortion. It has been estimated that as many as 5 per cent of conceptions are lost through ABO incompatibility. This phenomenon is not surprising, since the type O mother, for example, has "natural" antibody against type A and B antigens of fetal red cells and other tissues, including perhaps the placenta, which is largely of fetal genotype.

In the Rhesus (Rh) system, unlike the ABO blood-group system, the mother does not naturally carry antibodies against the types of Rhesus antigens that she does not possess. Trouble develops only if the mother becomes sensitized to what for her is a foreign antigen entering her system in the form of red cells from the fetus that contains a different Rhesus antigen through inheritance from the father. Sensitization of the mother is accomplished by actual bleeding from the fetus into the mother. Traumatic delivery is particularly likely to cause entry of fetal red cells into the maternal circulation. Sensitive methods based on the demonstration of red cells containing fetal hemoglobin can detect the presence of as little as 1 cc. of fetal blood distributed in the mother's circulation. In subsequent pregnancies, if the fetus is again incompatible, the mother's titer of anti-Rh antibody may rise briskly, and the damaging effect on the infant may result in the characteristic clinical picture of erythroblastosis fetalis. See Fig. 5.1.

About 15 per cent of Caucasians are Rhesus negative. Erythroblastosis fetalis would be much more frequent than it is if no other factors

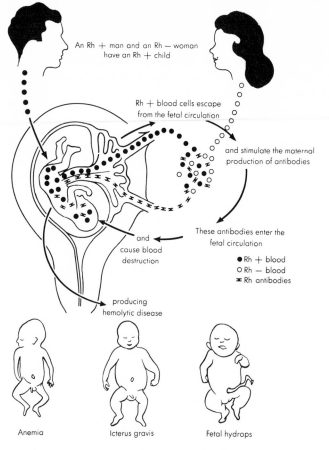

An Rh + man and an Rh − woman
have an Rh + child

Rh + blood cells escape
from the fetal circulation

and stimulate the maternal
production of antibodies

These antibodies enter the
fetal circulation

● Rh + blood
○ Rh − blood
✖ Rh antibodies

and
cause blood
destruction

producing
hemolytic disease

Anemia   Icterus gravis   Fetal hydrops

Fig. 5.1. The mechanism of *erythroblastosis fetalis*. Redrawn from Potter, *Rh: Its Relation to Congenital Hemolytic Disease and to Intragroup Transfusion Reactions* (Year Book, 1947).

were involved. One factor is undoubtedly the occurrence of feto-maternal bleeds; many Rhesus-incompatible pregnancies pass without the occurrence of such sensitizing bleeds. Another important factor protecting against Rhesus sensitization is accompanying ABO incompatibility. If the red blood cells that bleed from the fetus to the mother are of a different ABO blood type than the mother's, the natural antibody of the mother is likely to knock them out before they can incite sensitization.

The main offender in the Rhesus type of erythroblastosis fetalis is D. It seems to have greater antigenic propensities than the antigens C and E. Obviously, once erythroblastosis has occurred, the risk that future children of an Rh-negative mother and an Rh-positive father is 100 per cent if the father is DD but is only 50 per cent if he is Dd. Since in various populations some CDE combinations are more frequent than others, a probabilistic estimate of whether the father is DD or Dd can be obtained from the reactions with anti-C, anti-c, and anti-E antiserums. (Unfortunately no anti-d antiserum is available.) For example, if the father is an Englishman and reacts to anti-C, anti-D, and anti-e, but not to anti-c and anti-E, he must have CDe on one chromosome. The other chromosome may carry either CDe or Cde. Since in English populations CDe is about 41 times more common than Cde, it is likely that the man is homozygous DD (i.e., CDe/CDe).

The sex ratio

The ratio of males to females observed at birth is called the secondary sex ratio and is about 1.06 in whites in the United States. The primary sex ratio, that of the zygotes, is considerably higher, perhaps 1.30. The reason that Y-bearing sperm have an advantage over the X-bearing sperm in fertilization is unknown. Whatever the explanation, sex chromatin studies of early embryos show an excess of males in a ratio of about 1.3 to females. What accounts for the decline in the ratio between conception and birth? One possibility is that a proportion of male zygotes succumb to X-linked recessive lethals, but there is little direct evidence to support this plausible explanation. Another possibility is that the female with two X chromosomes enjoys heterotic vigor. Certainly the female has a greater survival throughout the span of life, both intra- and extra-uterine. The two sexes become numerically equal in middle life and in the older age groups women are more numerous than men.

Twins

About 1 per cent of all pregnancies in whites in the United States are twin pregnancies (counting only those terminating in live births). Therefore about 2 per cent of all newborn babies are twins. Since twins have a somewhat reduced chance of surviving the first year of life as compared to nontwins, the frequency of twins at age one year and older is about 1.9 per cent.

It is well known that twins are of two types. Dizygotic, two-egg, or fraternal twins result when two ova are produced at about the same time and both are fertilized. Monozygotic, one-egg, or identical twins result from the splitting of the zygote at an early stage. Monozygotic twins are of course genetically identical, barring somatic mutation. Dizygotic twins are gentically no more similar than ordinary sibs.

Monozygotic twins are of course either both male or both female. Dizygotic twins are of like sex or of unlike sex in approximately equal frequency. All twins of unlike sex are dizygotic, but twins of like sex may be of either type.

In 1901 Weinberg, a physician in Stuttgart, suggested a method of predicting the proportion of like-sexed twins that are monozygotic

Dizygotic twins have an about equal probability of being of like or of unlike sex. If n is the number of twins of unlike sex in a randomly ascertained series, then that same number n of the twins of like sex are also dizygotic; the remainder of the twins of like sex are monozygotic. In this country, for example, about 31 per cent of white twins are of unlike sex and therefore dizygotic. The remaining 69 per cent, the group of twins of like sex, includes another 31 per cent that are dizygotic. The remaining 38 per cent are monozygotic.

Monozygotic twinning shows almost no effect from the mother's age. Dizygotic twinning, on the other hand, is more frequent in older mothers. The frequency of twinning varies in different ethnic stocks, even when allowance is made for variations in the average age of mothers. In the 1950's whites in the United States had about 10 twin pregnancies per 1000, and nonwhites (mainly Negroes) had over 13.5 twin pregnancies per 1000. Almost all the excess twin pregnancies in the nonwhites were dizygotic. The racial differences in the frequency of dizygotic twinning may be evidence for genetic factors. That twinning shows a familial aggregation is further evidence of genetic factors. The propensity for dizygotic twinning is, of course, expressed only in females; females from high twinning families have an increased chance of bearing dizygotic twins. Males of such families may transmit this propensity to their daughters, although they do not sire dizygotic twins with increased frequency.

Environmental factors probably also influence the rate of twinning since the same ethnic stock in different habitats may show different rates. Furthermore, there was a significant decline in the rate of twinning in white people in the United States in the period from 1922 to 1958. In Sweden there has been a decline in twinning over the last two centuries.

The twin method was proposed by Francis Galton in 1876 as a means of distinguishing between environment and heredity, nurture and nature, in the determination of human variation. The concordance method (see p. 136) compares the degree of similarity of monozygotic twins to that of dizygotic twins of like sex, and compares the similarity of monozygotic twins that have been reared together to those that have been reared apart. The method obviously requires precise diagnosis of zygosity. Two methods of zygosity diagnosis are available: examination of the placenta and the similarity method, including skin grafting.

The developing zygote invests itself in two membrances, an inner (the amnion) and an outer (the chorion). In the case of dizygotic twins each twin has completely separate membranes, although when implantation is close together the two placentas may fuse. A significant proportion of monozygotic twins also have two chorions and two amnions, and some have two placentas. (See Fig. 5.2.) All mono-

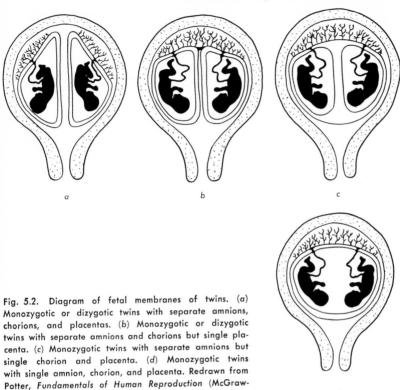

Fig. 5.2. Diagram of fetal membranes of twins. (a) Monozygotic or dizygotic twins with separate amnions, chorions, and placentas. (b) Monozygotic or dizygotic twins with separate amnions and chorions but single placenta. (c) Monozygotic twins with separate amnions but single chorion and placenta. (d) Monozygotic twins with single amnion, chorion, and placenta. Redrawn from Potter, *Fundamentals of Human Reproduction* (McGraw-Hill, 1948).

chorionic twins are monozygotic, and about 70 per cent of monozygotic twins have one chorion. Only in these cases is an unequivocal diagnosis of monozygosity possible on the basis of placental findings.

The similarity method, however, is usually the only one available for zygosity diagnosis and is more reliable than placental examination. However, as in many other situations in human genetics the conclusion is based on probability. Although monozygosity can be excluded, it can be established only with a certain probability, and never with absolute certainty. Objective single-gene traits such as blood groups and serum protein groups are used. The objective markers are the same as those used for linkage studies (see Chapter 3). Morphologic characteristics such as eye color, nose configuration, ear form, and others are less reliable. Ridge counts, a quantitative evaluation of the fingerprints (see p. 110) under polygenic control, can be used in zygosity diagnosis. Methods of mathematically estimating the probability that a given set of twins is monozygotic are reviewed on p. 107.

The last court of appeal in zygosity diagnosis is skin grafting. Reciprocal grafts should, of course, "take" in monozygotic twins and will not "take" in dizygotic twins. It is doubtful that vascular communications in dizygotic twins often lead to immune tolerance so that reciprocal skin grafts would be successful. However, there is no extensive experience with skin grafting in twins.

In cattle, the female of a pair of twins of unlike sex may develop into what is called a *freemartin*. The external genitalia are female in type, but the ovaries do not develop normally and the animal is sterile. A freemartin is formed only if fusion of fetal membranes takes place leading to cross-circulation. Hormones from the male were thought to be responsible for the changes in the female co-twin. However, recent work demonstrates actual germ-cell chimerism. No exactly comparable situation is known in man.

It is certain that vascular exchange between dizygotic human twins occurs, however, since chimerism of blood type has been recognized. Several examples have been found in which a dizygotic twin had a minor population of red cells with a blood group different from that of the majority. Primordial blood cells from the co-twin colonized the chimera twin in fetal life. In all instances tested the chimera twin could be shown to have developed immune tolerance and would accept a skin graft from the other twin. Sometimes both, and sometimes only one, of a pair of twins showed chimerism. Precursors of white cells may become grafted into a dizygotic co-twin by the same mechanism. Male twins have been found that had female co-twins and that showed polymorphonuclear leukocytes with the "drumstick" (p. 12) characteristic of the female. In some instances study of the chromosomes of leukocytes has shown the karyotype of the opposite sex, i.e., some XY cells in a female co-twin.

In 1895 Hellin pointed out that the frequency of triplets should be approximately the square of the frequency of twins and the frequency of quadruplets approximately the frequency of twins to the third power. Observed frequencies agree rather closely with those predicted by "Hellin's law."

Congenital malformations ("birth defects")

The term *congenital* is not synonymous with the term *hereditary*. *Congenital* means "present at birth." Malformations evident at birth and therefore congenital may be overwhelmingly genetic in their cause, or, on the contrary, may be overwhelmingly determined by extrinsic factors (see p. 86). Furthermore, not all genetic disorders are congenital—at least in terms of the phenotypic change being evident at birth. For example, in Huntington's chorea the fundamental defect is presumably present in the nervous system at birth, but the phenotypic manifestations may not be discernible until the age of 60 or older.

Hereditary, heritable, and *inherited* are essentially synonymous terms. A case of hereditary disease occurring as the result of a new mutation is heritable, although not inherited unless one considers that the occurrence of the mutation in the germ cell of a parent and subsequent passage to the offspring constitutes inheritance.

Aside from new mutations there are other genetic disorders that are usually not inherited, namely many of the chromosomal aberrations. Some chromosomal aberrations, however, are inherited. For example, there is a 50-50 chance that an offspring of a Mongoloid idiot will also be a Mongoloid idiot. The 15-21 translocation responsible for multiple cases of mongolism in some families is hereditary.

Strictly speaking *familial* is not synonymous with *hereditary* or *genetic* since nongenetic factors can account for familial aggregation. In the past *familial* was the term used for recessive disorders since they tend to occur in multiple sibs with normal parents and *hereditary* was the term used for dominant disorders. Obviously, a recessive disorder is as genuinely inherited as is a dominant one. Recessive inheritance is inheritance from both parents.

The causes of birth defects

Several congenital malformations have a relatively simple genetic basis, e.g., autosomal recessive acheiropody (absence of hands and feet), which has been observed only in Brazil (Fig. 5.3).

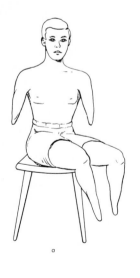

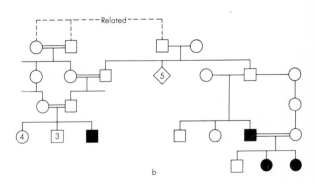

Fig. 5.3. (a) Acheiropody, a recessive trait that to date has been observed only in Brazil. (b) Pedigree.

a

b

A few congenital malformations have a relatively simple environmental or extrinsic cause. Two examples are the malformations of the heart, eyes, and other organs due to rubella (German measles) occurring in the first 12 weeks of pregnancy, and phocomelia ("seal limbs") and other anomalies due to the consumption of thalidomide, a tranquilizer and sedative, during early pregnancy.

The majority of congenital malformations, e.g., cleft palate, harelip, clubfoot, anencephaly, and congenital heart malformations are probably the result of a collaboration of genetic and environmental factors, none of which is understood in any great detail.

Experiments with teratogenic agents in animals suggest that vulnerability to the effects of these agents is genetically determined. For example, cortisone will induce cleft palate in a high proportion of offspring in one strain of mice and in only a low proportion in another strain. The likelihood of producing a particular malformation with the administration of a teratogenic agent to a pregnant animal is often related to the frequency of that malformation as a "spontaneous" occurrence in the particular strain of animal. Nothing is known about genetic differences in susceptibility to chemical teratogens in man. In fact, few chemicals teratogenic to man have been demonstrated. This does not mean, of course, that many do not exist. Congenital malformations due to thalidomide were rather quickly recognized because of the dramatic nature of the malformation, phocomelia, which, furthermore, occurs very rarely as a "spontaneous" malformation. On the other hand, as much as a tenfold increase in the frequency of a more commonplace malformation such as cleft palate or harelip could be produced by a given chemical and not be recognized.

The importance of genetic factors in congenital malformations is underscored by the pronounced species differences in teratogenesis. Many agents, teratogenic in certain experimental animals, even in small dosage, give no evidence of being teratogenic in man. The "animal screening" of new drugs for possible teratogenic effects when administered to pregnant women is difficult because of these differences in species. Possibly studies in nonhuman primates will give more pertinent information on teratogenic effects of chemicals used in man.

Some specific human malformations have been observed to occur with greater frequency in some races than in others. For example, polydactyly is about 10 times more frequent in Negroes than in whites, and preauricular sinus may be about equally more frequent in Negroes. On the other hand, severe malformation of the nervous system, e.g., anencephaly, is rarer in Negroes than in whites. The *total number* of congenital malformations—a substantial amount of data is available for Caucasians, Negroes, and Japanese—tends to be about the same in various races.

References

Benirschke, Kurt, "Accurate Recording of Twin Placentation: A Plea to the Obstetrician," *Obstet. Gynecol., 18* (1961), 334-47.

Corner, G. W., "The Observed Embryology of Human Single-Ovum Twins and Other Multiple Births," *Am. J. Obstet. Gynecol., 70* (1955), 933-51.

Fishbein, Morris, ed., *Birth Defects.* Philadelphia: J. B. Lippincott Co., 1963.

Markert, Clement, *Developmental Genetics.* Englewood Cliffs, N.J.: Prentice-Hall, Inc., 1964.

Six

Genes in Families and in Populations—
Mathematical Aspects

Hardy and Weinberg considered gene frequency the pertinent variable in population genetics. The alleles at a given locus are thought of as occurring in a "gene pool." Under conditions of random mating, as is assumed by the Hardy–Weinberg principle, two alleles meet in the diploid organism in frequencies that are the product of the individual gene frequencies. For example, in a two-allele system if p is the relative frequency (or proportion) of the dominant allele A, q the relative frequency (or proportion) of the recessive allele a, and $p + q = 1$, then in a randomly mating population the frequencies of the three genotypes are p^2 (for AA), $2pq$ (for Aa), and q^2 (for aa). (See Lawrence E. Mettler's *Population Genetics and Evolution* in this series.)

The Hardy–Weinberg principle, the cornerstone of population genetics, states that the relative proportions of genotypes with respect to one autosomal locus remain constant from one generation to another—for example, the three genotypes AA, Aa, and aa in a system with two alleles A and a. Like all generalizations in science, this one is based on certain simplifying assumptions and disregards certain factors (such as mutation and selection) that disturb the equilibrium. The Hardy–Weinberg equilibrium is the basis for a consideration of the influence of these factors

88

on the relative proportions of the three genotypes in successive generations. The algebraic example in Table 6.1 shows that genotype frequencies indeed remain constant from one generation to the next.

Table 6.1. The Hardy-Weinberg equilibrium.

(a) Characteristics of the parental generation.

ALLELIC GENES	ASSIGNED FREQUENCY	NUMERICAL EXAMPLE	GENOTYPES	FREQUENCIES IN POPULATION	NUMERICAL EXAMPLE
A	p	.90	AA	p^2	81
a	q	.10	Aa	$2pq$	18
			aa	q^2	1
TOGETHER		1.00	ALL TYPES	1	100

(b) Offspring from random matings.

PARENTS ♂ ♀	FREQUENCY OF MATING TYPE	FREQUENCY OF OFFSPRING* AA	Aa	aa	NUMERICAL EXAMPLE AA	Aa	aa
$AA \times AA$	p^4	p^4	—	—	6561	0	0
$AA \times Aa$ / $Aa \times AA$	$4p^3q$	$2p^3q$	$2p^3q$	—	1458	1458	0
$AA \times aa$ / $aa \times AA$	$2p^2q^2$	—	$2p^2q^2$	—	0	162	0
$Aa \times Aa$	$4p^2q^2$	p^2q^2	$2p^2q^2$	p^2q^2	81	162	81
$Aa \times aa$ / $aa \times Aa$	$4pq^3$	—	$2pq^3$	$2pq^3$	0	18	18
$aa \times aa$	q^4	—	—	q^4	0	0	1
ALL TYPES	1	p^2	$2pq$	q^2	8100	1800	100

* The AA column adds up to $p^4 + 2p^3q + p^2q^2$, or $p^2(p^2 + 2pq + q^2)$.
The Aa column adds up to $2p^3q + 4p^2q^2 + 2pq^3$, or $2pq(p^2 + 2pq + q^2)$.
The aa column adds up to $p^2q^2 + 2pq^3 + q^4$, or $q^2(p^2 + 2pq + q^2)$.

The analytic usefulness of the fundamental proportions of genotypes $(p^2 : 2pq : q^2)$ is illustrated by the fact that knowing the frequency of the recessive phenotype (q^2) one can calculate the proportion of heterozygotes $(2pq)$, which is relatively large even if the recessive phenotype is rare. In the example of Table 6.1 the homozygotes aa are only 1 in 100, but the heterozygotes Aa are 18 in 100. Albinism, a recessive trait, occurs about 1 in 10,000 persons (q^2). The frequency of the recessive allele (q) is then $\sqrt{1/10,000}$, or 1/100. The frequency of the dominant allele (p) is $1 - 1/100$, or 99/100. The frequency of heterozygous carriers of albinism $(2pq)$ is $2 \times 1/100 \times 99/100$, or about 1 in 50.

For X-linked traits the phenotype frequency in males is equal to the gene frequency. In a two-allele system the male must be one of only two phenotypes and genotypes. The trait must either be present or be absent and the frequencies are p and q, respectively. It does not matter, furthermore, whether the trait is recessive or dominant in the female; in either case the phenotype frequency in the male is identical to the gene frequency.

Rare X-linked dominant traits occur about twice as frequently in females as in males. Females affected by a dominant X-linked trait are of two types—homozygotes with a frequency p^2 and heterozygotes with a frequency $2pq$. The frequency of affected males is p. The ratio of affected females to affected males is, then, $\dfrac{p^2 + 2pq}{p}$. For a rare X-linked dominant trait (such as vitamin D-resistant rickets) p^2 is negligibly small and q is almost 1. Therefore, the F:M ratio becomes about $2p/p$ (affected females twice as frequent as affected males). With more frequent X-linked dominants, such is no longer the case. Thus, for the Xg^a blood group, about 64 per cent of men are Xg(a+) and about 88 per cent of women are Xg(a+).

Mating frequencies

Under conditions of random mating, which is an assumption of the Hardy–Weinberg principle, the frequency of matings of different types is the product of the frequencies of the individuals making up the mating. This is illustrated in part b of Table 6.1. If p^2 is the frequency of AA persons, then $p^2 \times p^2$, or p^4, is the frequency of $AA \times AA$ matings. Since $2pq$ is the frequency of Aa persons, the frequency of $AA \times Aa$ matings is $p^2 \times 2pq \times 2$, or $4p^3q$. Note that the product is doubled in this case because the $AA \times Aa$ mating may be either $AA\,\male \times Aa\,\female$ or $AA\,\female \times Aa\,\male$. When the genotypes of the parents differ the product is doubled to arrive at the mating frequency.

Bias of ascertainment

A skillful college genetics teacher announced to his all-male class of 129 students that they would determine the normal human sex ratio by adding the numbers of males and females in the sibships from which each of them came. The data were recorded as shown in Table 6.2.

This example serves to illustrate the fact that when sibships are ascertained because of the occurrence in them of one person with a

Table 6.2. A class experiment.*

	MALE	FEMALE
Abrams	1	1
Adams	1	0
Allen	3	2
Anderson	2	1
...	...	...
...	...	...
...	...	...
Young	2	0
Ziegler	1	2
TOTAL	228	95
GRAND TOTAL	323	

* What, the professor asked his class, is the sex ratio in this sample of families? The first reply was $\frac{228}{95}$, a preposterously high sex ratio. The true sex ratio is obtained by removing the probands from the calculation. The ratio then becomes $\frac{89}{85}$, or 1.04.

given trait (in this example, maleness was the trait) the proportion of persons affected by said trait in the families cannot be expected to agree with the true proportion if the proband is included in the enumeration. Inclusion of the proband loads the results in favor of the trait. If all human sibships had 100 individuals or even 10, the effect would be much less pronounced. But obviously all *ascertainable* one-child sibships will have 100 per cent trait-bearers, two-child sibships will have 67 per cent trait bearers (when the fundamental probability is 50 per cent), three-child sibships will have 57 per cent trait bearers, and so on.

Testing the recessive hypothesis

In segregation analysis of autosomal dominant traits, families for study are usually ascertained through a single affected parent; the proportion of all offspring with the trait can be expected to fit the 50 per cent figure. However, in studying rare autosomal recessive traits one usually can recognize those families that have both parents heterozygous and therefore have a 25 per cent chance of having affected children, *only* when at least one child is affected.

Consider a group of 16 families with 2 children in each and with both parents heterozygous for a rare recessive gene (Fig. 6.1a). In these 16 families chances are that 4 of the 16 first-born children will

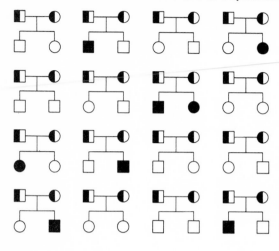

Fig. 6.1a. In a group of 16 families, each with both parents heterozygous for a recessive gene and each with two children, the findings will be as indicated here. The solid symbols indicate offspring affected by a simple recessive trait.

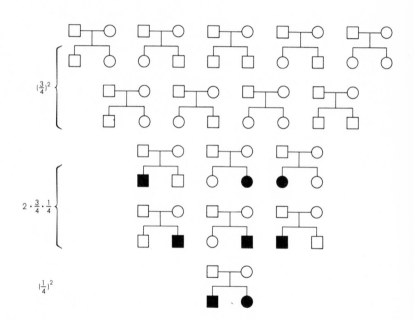

Fig. 6.1b. Only 7 of the 16 families will be ascertained when the families are found because of at least one affected child, as is usually the case.

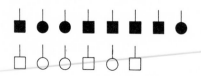

Fig. 6.1c. The proportion of children affected in the ascertained families is not 1 in 4 but rather 8 in 14 (57 per cent).

be affected. Likewise, chances are that 4 of the 16 second-born will be affected, but since this is an event independent of the first, in only one of the 16 families ($\frac{1}{4} \times \frac{1}{4} = \frac{1}{16}$) will *both* children be affected. These expectancies are schematized in a second way in Fig. 6.2.

Since the mode of ascertainment is through affected children, only 7 of the 16 families can be recognized (Fig. 6.1b). The proportion of affected children in these families is found to be not $\frac{1}{4}$ but $\frac{8}{14}$ (57 per cent) (Fig. 6.1c). The general expression for unascertained sibships is $(\frac{3}{4})^s$, where s is sibship size and $\frac{3}{4}$ is the probability of the dominant phenotype. In Fig. 6.3, segregation in 3-child families (with both parents heterozygous) is illustrated.

It will be noted that the unascertained sibships are cut off the end of the binomial expansion $(d + r)^s$ where d is the probability of the dominant phenotype (in this instance $\frac{3}{4}$), r the probability of the reces-

	First child			
	Normal	Normal	Normal	Affected
Normal				One affected
Normal				One affected
Normal				One affected
Affected	One affected	One affected	One affected	Both affected

(Second child — row label)

Fig. 6.2. Expected distribution of a recessive trait in two-child families, when both parents are heterozygous.

Fig. 6.3. Segregation of a simple recessive trait (solid symbols) in families of three children with both parents heterozygous. Here and in Fig. 6.5 the symbols may, of course, represent either males or females. Redrawn from Li, *Human Genetics* (McGraw-Hill, 1961).

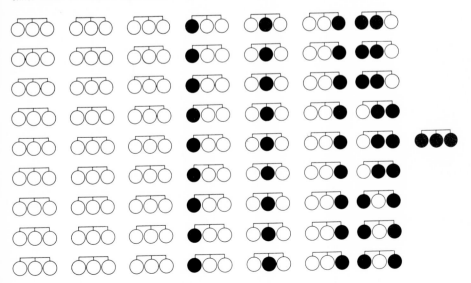

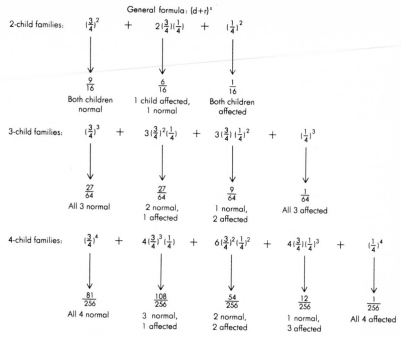

Fig. 6.4. Various proportions of sibs affected by an autosomal recessive trait in families of various sizes with both parents heterozygous.

sive phenotype ($\frac{1}{4}$), and s the sibship size. Figure 6.4 gives the formulas and the proportion of families with various numbers of affected children, for families of 2, 3, and 4 sibs. For five-sib families the formula is as follows:

$$(\tfrac{3}{4})^5 + 5(\tfrac{3}{4})^4(\tfrac{1}{4}) + 10(\tfrac{3}{4})^3(\tfrac{1}{4})^2 + 10(\tfrac{3}{4})^2(\tfrac{1}{4})^3 + 5(\tfrac{3}{4})(\tfrac{1}{4})^4 + (\tfrac{1}{4})^5$$

and so on.

The coefficients in the binomial expansion are easily recalled from Pascal's triangle:

$$
\begin{array}{ccccccccccccc}
 & & & & & & 1 & & & & & & \\
 & & & & & 1 & & 1 & & & & & \\
 & & & & 1 & & 2 & & 1 & & & & \\
 & & & 1 & & 3 & & 3 & & 1 & & & \\
 & & 1 & & 4 & & 6 & & 4 & & 1 & & \\
 & 1 & & 5 & & 10 & & 10 & & 5 & & 1 & \\
1 & & 6 & & 15 & & 20 & & 15 & & 6 & & 1 \\
\end{array}
$$

etc.

Or they can be derived from the formula

$$\frac{s!}{a!b!}$$

Table 6.3. Predicted values for testing recessive hypothesis by Lenz-Hogben method.

SIBSHIP SIZE (s)	PROPORTION OF SUCH SIBSHIPS THAT CANNOT BE ASCERTAINED ($x = (3/4)^s$)	PROPORTION OF SIBSHIPS THAT CAN BE ASCERTAINED ($y = 1 - (3/4)^s$)	PROPORTION OF AFFECTED IN ASCERTAINED SIBSHIPS (z)	AVERAGE NUMBER AFFECTED (sz)
1	3/4	1/4	1	1
2	$(3/4)^2$ = 9/16	7/16	8/14 (0.5714)	1.143
3	$(3/4)^3$ = 27/64	37/64	48/111 (0.4324)	1.297
4	$(3/4)^4$ = 81/256	175/256	256/700 (0.3657)	1.463
5	$(3/4)^5$ = 243/1,024	781/1,024	(0.3278)	1.639
6	$(3/4)^6$ = 729/4,096	3,367/4,096	(0.3041)	1.825
7	$(3/4)^7$ = 2,187/16,384	14,197/16,384	(0.2885)	2.020
8	$(3/4)^8$ = 6,561/65,536	58,975/65,536	(0.2778)	2.223
9	$(3/4)^9$ = 19,683/262,144	242,461/262,144	(0.2703)	2.433
10	$(3/4)^{10}$ = 59,049/1,048,576	989,527/1,048,576	(0.2649)	2.649
11	$(3/4)^{11}$ = 177,147/4,194,304	4,017,157/4,194,304	(0.2610)	2.871
12	$(3/4)^{12}$ = 531,441/16,777,216	16,245,775/16,777,216	(0.2582)	3.098

where s is the total number of sibs and a and b are the number of sibs of each of the two types.

If every case of a rare autosomal recessive trait were ascertained in a population, then the distribution of families according to proportions with the several different numbers of children affected would be as indicated above. This form of detection is referred to as complete, or truncate, ascertainment. Using the principles outlined above, Fritz Lenz of Germany and Lancelot Hogben of England, among others, devised the so-called Lenz–Hogben method to test whether the proportion of affected sibs agrees with the one-quarter ratio. The proportion of affected children differs with families of different size. One counts up the total number of children and the number affected in sibships of the various sizes; these figures are the "observed." One then multiplies the total number of sibships of a particular size by the proportion expected to be affected with that size

Table 6.4. Alkaptonuria families with both parents unaffected.

NUMBER OF SIBS	NUMBER OF SIBSHIPS	NUMBER OF SIBS AFFECTED	
		Observed	Expected
1	5	5	5
2	8	10	9.14
3	5	8	6.49
4	2	4	2.93
5	3	4	4.92
6	3	8	5.47
7	2	5	4.04
8	3	5	6.67
9	1	4	2.43
10	1	2	2.65
11	3	7	8.61
14	1	4	3.56
TOTAL	37	66	61.91

of sibship (sz); this is the "expected." "Observed" is then compared with "expected." Statistical methods for determining whether "observed" differs significantly from "expected" are to be found in many textbooks on human genetics.

Table 6.3 presents the values used in calculating the "expected" value. Table 6.4 presents data on alkaptonuria, an autosomal recessive condition that has been discussed in other connections (p. 69).

Incomplete ascertainment

Ascertainment is often incomplete, and the probability that a given family enters the sample bears some relationship to the number of sibs affected. For example, in three-child families, if all three sibs are affected with a rare recessively inherited disease, the likelihood of that family coming to the attention of one of the facilities whose records are screened for cases—e.g., a hospital, a crippled children's agency, or a practicing specialist—may be greater than if only one of the three sibs is affected. Assume, for example, that the chance that a three-sib family in which two or three children are affected will come to attention is two and three times, respectively, the chance that a three-sib family with only one affected child will come to attention. The distribution of ascertained families of three-sibs size which in the model of truncate, or complete, ascertainment was 27:9:1, becomes in this model 27:18:3 (Fig. 6.5a). The proper correction is to remove from each family one affected sib and determine the proportion of affected children among the remaining sibs (Fig. 6.5b). The general formula is:

$$p = \frac{R - N}{T - N}$$

where R is the total number of individuals affected by the recessive condition (in the example of Fig. 6.5); N is the number of ascertained sibships (in the example, 48); and T is the total number of sibs (in the example, 144). In the example,

$$p = \frac{74 - 48}{144 - 48} = \frac{24}{96} = \frac{1}{4}$$

In practice, ascertainment is frequently neither complete (for which the Lenz–Hogben correction is appropriate) nor related as a simple integer to the number of affected sibs (for which the second correction just decribed is appropriate). The ascertainment is often of some intermediate type, and its precise nature may be unclear. In such instances, both types of correction can be applied. When this is done, it is likely that the segregation ratio estimated by the Lenz–Hogben method is higher than 0.25 and that estimated by the second method is lower than 0.25. The fact that the value 0.25 is spanned by the two corrections can be taken as support of the recessive hypothesis.

In summary, the Lenz–Hogben correction is appropriate to truncate ascertainment in which either complete ascertainment or random sampling of affected *families* is achieved. The second type of correction is applicable to so-called single ascertainment, which provides a ran-

Fig. 6.5. (a) The observed sibships of size three when the probability of detecting sibships with two and three members affected by a recessive trait is, respectively, two and three times the probability of detecting a sibship with one affected member. This is termed single ascertainment. (b) The method of correction is to delete one affected member from each sibship. Thus, 24 affected among a total of 96 children, or 1 in 4, is found. Redrawn from Li, *Human Genetics* (McGraw-Hill, 1961).

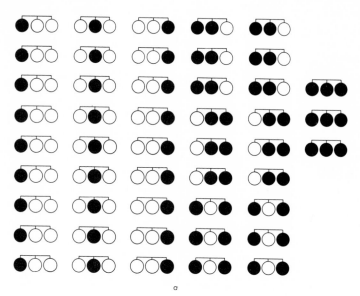

a

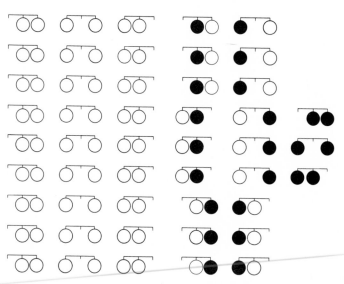

b

dom sample of affected *individuals*, and a sample of families weighted in direct proportion to the number of sibs affected.

A more comprehensive discussion of these problems, which fall into the area of statistical genetics called *segregation analysis*, is beyond the scope of this book.

Working out the mode of inheritance of a polymorphic trait

A useful illustration of the methods by which one determines the mode of transmission of a polymorphic trait is provided by studies on the metabolism of isoniazid (INH), a drug taken orally for the treatment of tuberculosis, and acetylated in the liver. The acetylated form is inactive against the tuberculosis organism, and the process is therefore referred to as INH inactivation. The fact that some persons are rapid inactivators and others slow inactivators immediately suggested a genetic basis for the variations. Next it was necessary to determine whether people fall into two clearly discontinuous classes with respect to INH inactivation rate.

A test was devised, consisting of orally administering a standard amount of isoniazid per unit of body weight and measuring the level of free, or nonacetylated, INH in the blood 6 hours later. The rapid inactivator had a low level and the slow inactivator a high level of free INH after 6 hours. Furthermore, the persons tested fell into two distinct classes with essentially no overlap (Fig. 6.6). No difference in frequency in males as compared to females was found; thus, the genetic control is probably autosomal.

The frequency of the alleles controlling the two alternative phenotypes was then determined. The phenotype frequencies were found

Fig. 6.6. Two classes of persons according to rate of acetylation ("inactivation") of isoniazid (INH). Based on Evans, Storey, and Mc-Kusick, *Bull. Johns Hopkins Hosp.*, 108 (1961), 60-66.

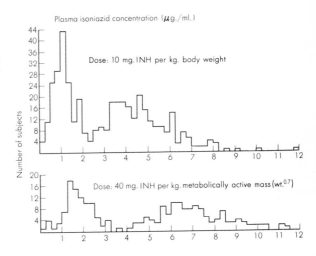

Table 6.5. Frequency of mating types.*

| MATING TYPE | | RELATIVE FREQUENCY | |
Father A	Mother B	$A \times B$	Simplest expression
I Dominant phenotype $p^2 + 2pq$	$\times$ dominant phenotype $p^2 + 2pq$	$p^4 + 4p^3q + 4p^2q^2$	$p^2(p + 2q)^2 = p^2(1 + q)^2$†
II Dominant phenotype $p^2 + 2pq$	$\times$ recessive phenotype q^2	$2p^2q^2 + 4pq^3$	$2pq^2(p + 2q) = 2pq^2(1 + q)$†
Recessive phenotype q^2	$\times$ dominant phenotype $p^2 + 2pq$		
III Recessive phenotype q^2	$\times$ recessive phenotype q^2	q^4	q^4

* See Table 6.6.
† Since $p + q = 1$, $p^2(p + q + q)^2 = p^2(1 + q)^2$, and $2pq^2(p + q + q) = 2pq^2(1 + q)$.

to be about 50 per cent slow inactivator and 50 per cent rapid inactivator. The frequency of the recessive phenotype, q^2 of the Hardy–Weinberg formula, is then .50 and q, the recessive gene frequency, is about .70.

Family studies provide the answer to the question of which phenotype is the recessive one. A randomly selected group of families in which both parents and one or more children are available for phenotyping is studied. Two main approaches are used in the analysis of the data. Firstly, one asks whether the observed proportions of parental mating types agree better with what one would expect if slow inactivation is dominant or if slow inactivation is recessive. Secondly, one asks whether the proportions of slow-inactivator offspring observed from each of the three possible parental mating types agree better with the dominant or the recessive hypothesis.

Obviously three parental mating types can occur: (1) rapid inactivator × rapid inactivator, (2) rapid inactivator × slow inactivator, and (3) slow inactivator × slow inactivator. Of the second mating type there are two varieties depending on whether the father or the mother is the slow inactivator. In Table 6.5 are shown the proportions of the three mating types expected for the general case.

If slow inactivation is considered dominant, the observed frequencies of the three mating types agree poorly with expected results. However, when slow inactivation is assumed to be recessive, the hypothesis is supported by the agreement of observed results with expected results (Table 6.6).

Table 6.6. Mating types in INH data.

PHENOTYPIC MATINGS	EXPECTED FREQUENCY OF MATING*	EXPECTED OCCURRENCE IN 53 MATINGS	OBSERVED OCCURRENCE
$S \times S$	0.27	14.5	16
$R \times S$	0.50	26.4	24
$R \times R$	0.23	12.1	13
TOTAL	1.00	53.0	53.0

* The hypothesis is *slow inactivation is recessive*. Hence the frequency of the gene for slow inactivation is 0.72 ($\sqrt{.52}$). The χ^2 test of agreement of observed with expected results gives a value of 0.964, with two degrees of freedom, corresponding to a p value greater than 0.5; i.e., the agreement is satisfactory.

Shown in Table 6.7 are the algebraic expressions for the proportion of children expected with each phenotype on the basis of the two hypotheses being tested. Table 6.8 shows that observations agreed well with the expected proportions of slow-inactivator offspring when

Table 6.7. Phenotype frequencies in children.

	MATING TYPES ♂ ♀	PARENTAL GENOTYPE FREQUENCIES	OFFSPRING			PROPORTION OF RECESSIVE OFFSPRING
			AA	Aa	aa	
I $D \times D$	$AA \times AA$	p^4	p^4	—	—	
	$\left.\begin{array}{l} AA \times Aa \\ Aa \times AA \end{array}\right\}$	$4p^3q$	$2p^3q$	$2p^3q$	—	
	$Aa \times Aa$	$4p^2q^2$	p^2q^2	$2p^2q^2$	$\boxed{p^2q^2}$	$\dfrac{q^2}{4q^2 + 4pq + p^2}$
II $D \times R$	$\left.\begin{array}{l} AA \times aa \\ aa \times AA \end{array}\right\}$	$2p^2q^2$	—	$2p^2q^2$	—	
	$\left.\begin{array}{l} Aa \times aa \\ aa \times Aa \end{array}\right\}$	$4pq^3$	—	$2pq^3$	$\boxed{2pq^3}$	$\dfrac{2q}{2p + 4q}$
III $R \times R$	$aa \times aa$	q^4	—	—	$\boxed{q^4}$	100%
TOTAL		$p^2 + 2pq + q^2$			$q^2(p^2 + 2pq + q^2)$	

Table 6.8. Proportion of rapid-inactivator and slow-inactivator children, when slow inactivation is assumed to be recessive.*

PHENOTYPIC MATINGS OF PARENTS	NUMBER OF CHILDREN	NUMBER OF CHILDREN OF EACH PHENOTYPE			
		Rapid		Slow	
		Expected	*Observed*	*Expected*	*Observed*
$S \times S$	51	nil	nil	51	51
$R \times S$	70	40.6	42	29.4	28
$R \times R$	38	31.3	31	6.7	7
	159		73		86

* The frequency of the gene for slow inactivation is estimated at 0.72 ($\sqrt{.52}$). The agreement of observed with expected is satisfactorily close.

slow inactivation was assumed to be recessive. Note in particular the complete absence of persons with the dominant phenotype among the offspring of two parents with the recessive phenotype when slow inactivation is considered recessive. If the same calculations are made, assuming that rapid inactivation is recessive, several children with the dominant phenotype are found from matings of two presumedly recessive parents.

The presumed dominant phenotype, rapid inactivation, is the result of either of two genotypes, the homozygote or the heterozygote. The average rate of inactivation in necessarily heterozygous persons (persons with dominant phenotype who are offspring of dominant × recessive matings) is slower than that in offspring of two rapid inactivator parents with no slow inactivator children. Thus, some dosage effect is demonstrable.

Furthermore, since the presence or absence of an enzyme or coenzyme is presumably responsible for rapid or slow inactivation, respectively, it is quite logical that slow inactivation (slow acetylation) should be the recessive phenotype.

The same type of analysis is applicable to other polymorphic traits, e.g., blood groups. Apparent inconsistencies, such as the occurrence of the dominant phenotype in an offspring of two parents with the recessive phenotype, may be explained either by misclassification of phenotype or by illegitimacy. The latter possibility can sometimes be demonstrated by multiple marker traits. Legitimacy can be excluded but never proved with complete certainty by marker traits.

Quantitative aspects of consanguinity

Mating is nonrandom, or assortative, if the probability of a particular type of mating is not dictated solely by the relative frequencies of the three genotypes in the population. Consanguineous marriages are nonrandom because the genotypes of closely related persons have an increased chance of being similar rather than representative of the general population.

The probability that two persons have a gene in common is referred to as the coefficient of relationship (r). Stated differently, it is the proportion of all genes that are identical by descent, in two given persons. In Fig. 6.7 the estimation of the coefficient is illustrated for

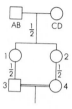

Fig. 6.7. Calculating the coefficient of relationship (r) of first cousins: $r = \frac{1}{8}$.

first cousins. The chance that allele A passes to 1 is $\frac{1}{2}$, and then to 3 is again $\frac{1}{2}$—in all, $\frac{1}{4}$. The chance that 4 gets allele A is also $\frac{1}{4}$. The chance that both 3 and 4 get allele A is $\frac{1}{4} \times \frac{1}{4}$, or $\frac{1}{16}$. The chance that both 3 and 4 get allele B is also $\frac{1}{16}$. The final probability that the same allele (either A or B) is present in first cousins is $\frac{1}{16} + \frac{1}{16}$, or $\frac{1}{8}$. On the average, one-eighth of the genes of first cousins are identical and are derived from the same ancestral source. See Fig. 6.8 for other examples and for illustration of use of the method of path coefficients.

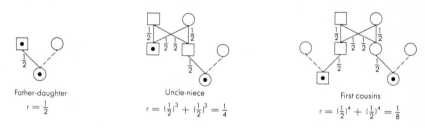

Father-daughter
$r = \frac{1}{2}$

Uncle-niece
$r = (\frac{1}{2})^3 + (\frac{1}{2})^3 = \frac{1}{4}$

First cousins
$r = (\frac{1}{2})^4 + (\frac{1}{2})^4 = \frac{1}{8}$

Fig. 6.8. The coefficient of relationship (r) of some other close relatives.

The coefficient of inbreeding (F) is the probability that the two genes at a given locus in a given individual are identical, that is, are derived from the same ancestor. Stated differently, it is the proportion of all loci that are homozygous in the given individual. If the coefficient of relationship of the parents is $\frac{1}{8}$ (as it is for first cousins), then the coefficient of inbreeding of the offspring is $\frac{1}{8} \times \frac{1}{2}$, or $\frac{1}{16}$. This follows because if gene A is given to the offspring by the father, the probability is $\frac{1}{2}$ that the mother will also give gene A to the offspring if she has it, and the probability that she has it is $\frac{1}{8}$. An alternative approach, that of path coefficients, counts the paths connecting the offspring with each common ancestor. In the case of the offspring of half first cousins there is one common ancestor, and five paths, each with a coefficient of $\frac{1}{2}$, connecting him with this common ancestor. Hence, F is $(\frac{1}{2})^5$, or $\frac{1}{32}$. For the offspring of full first cousins there are two common ancestors; for each the coefficient is $(\frac{1}{2})^5$ and the total coefficient of inbreeding is $(\frac{1}{2})^5 + (\frac{1}{2})^5$, or $\frac{1}{16}$. On the average, in the offspring of a first-cousin marriage, one-sixteenth of the genes are present in homozygous state. The coefficient of inbreeding is presented schematically in Fig. 6.9.

Fig. 6.9. The coefficient of inbreeding (F) of the offspring of certain consanguineous matings.

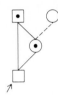

Offspring of
father-daughter
mating
$$F = \frac{1}{2} \cdot \frac{1}{2} = \frac{1}{4}$$

Offspring of
uncle-niece
mating
$$F = \frac{1}{2} \cdot \frac{1}{4} = \frac{1}{8}$$
or
$$(\tfrac{1}{2})^4 + (\tfrac{1}{2})^4 = \frac{1}{8}$$

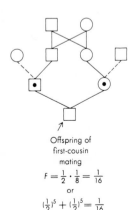

Offspring of
first-cousin
mating
$$F = \frac{1}{2} \cdot \frac{1}{8} = \frac{1}{16}$$
or
$$(\tfrac{1}{2})^5 + (\tfrac{1}{2})^5 = \frac{1}{16}$$

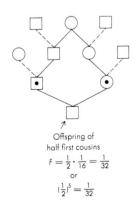

Offspring of
half first cousins
$$F = \frac{1}{2} \cdot \frac{1}{16} = \frac{1}{32}$$
or
$$(\tfrac{1}{2})^5 = \frac{1}{32}$$

The frequency of consanguinity in the parents of cases of autosomal recessive disorders is inversely related to the gene frequency. The mathematical formulation for this relationship is approximately:

$$k = \frac{c(1 + 15q)}{16q} = \frac{c}{16q} + \frac{15}{16}c$$

where k tells us how often it can be expected that sibships containing individuals homozygous for a recessive allele have parents who are first cousins;

c is the frequency of first-cousin marriages in the general population; and

q is the frequency of the recessive allele.

Since the second term in the formula above is usually small, it can be disregarded and the formula becomes simply $k = c/16q$.

In most of the United States today the frequency of first-cousin marriages is less than 1 in 1,000 ($<0.1\%$). With a recessive gene whose frequency is .01 (the frequency of homozygous affected being 1 in 10,000), the frequency of first-cousin parental matings is about 0.7 per cent. With a recessive gene whose frequency is .001, giving a frequency of the homozygous recessive of 1 in 1,000,000, the frequency of first-cousin parental matings is about 6 per cent.

The relationship between gene frequency and the frequency of parental consanguinity is well illustrated by the findings in Tay–Sachs disease, a degenerative central-nervous-system disease that leads to early death. Inherited as an autosomal recessive, the disorder is rather frequent in Jewish persons, especially those whose ancestors lived in northeastern Poland and southern Lithuania. The gene frequency in the Jewish population of New York City appears to be between .011 and .016, with about 1 in every 30 persons being a carrier. Among the parents of Jewish children with Tay–Sachs disease there is little or no increase in the rate of consanguinity when the parents had Polish-Lithuanian ancestry. What is probably the same disease occurs much more rarely in non-Jewish persons, but in these persons there is an appreciable increase in the frequency of consanguinity of parents of affected children.

Knowing the frequency of parental consanguinity in a series of cases of an autosomal recessive trait, and knowing the frequency of consanguinity in the general population, one can make a crude estimate of gene frequency by rearranging the formula given above in this manner:

$$q = \frac{c}{16k - 15c}$$

In Japan a calculation of the frequency of the gene that in the homozygous state causes absence of catalase in the blood was based on an estimate of 0.06 for c and of 0.59 for k. Thus, the gene frequency may be of the order of 0.005.

The probability that twins are monozygotic

The probability of monozygosity may be increased, and thereby also the efficiency of the similarity method (of Sheila Maynard-Smith and Lionel S. Penrose), if the genotype of the parents with respect to objective marker traits is taken into account. (See Fig. 6.10.) The following question is posed: Given twin A as found and given the other relatives as found, what is the probability that the twin B should be found identical in all the phenotypes tested if in fact they are dizygotic?

In England, where the family diagrammed in Fig. 6.10 lived, about 35 per cent of twins are dizygotic and of like sex. The chance (a priori probability) that twin B would be the same sex as A is then 0.35. The mating $A_2O \times OO$ will produce 50 per cent A_2 and 50 per cent O children. The chance of the second being A_2 like the first, even though they are dizygotic, is 0.50. The mating $Kk \times Kk$ will produce 25 per cent KK offspring. The chance that the second twin will be KK,

Fig. 6.10. Are these twins monozygotic? See text. Redrawn from Race and Sanger, *Blood Groups in Man* (Blackwell Scientific Publications, 1962).

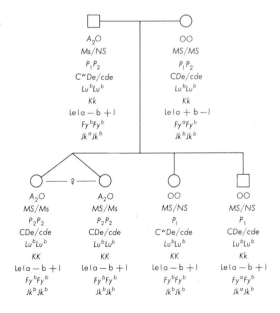

even if they are dizygotic, is then 0.25. The other probabilities are worked out in Table 6.9. The combined chance is the product of the separate chances: for dizygosity 0.00034, and for monozygosity 0.30. The relative probability of monozygosity is

$$\frac{0.30}{0.30 + 0.00034} = 0.9989$$

and the relative probability of dizygosity is

$$\frac{0.00034}{0.30 + 0.00034} = 0.0011$$

When the genotypes of the parents are not known, the probability of monozygosity can be estimated by a comparable method based on gene frequencies in the population from which the twins are derived.

Table 6.9. Probability of monozygosity.

Chance of like-sex dizygotic twins	0.35	Chance of monozygotic twins	0.30
Chance of dizygotic twins in this family having same		Chance of monozygotic twins in this family having same	
ABO groups	0.50	ABO groups	1.00
MNSs groups	0.50	MNSs groups	1.00
P groups	0.25	P groups	1.00
Rh groups	0.25	Rh groups	1.00
Kell groups	0.25	Kell groups	1.00
Duffy groups	0.50	Duffy groups	1.00
Kidd groups	0.50	Kidd groups	1.00
Combined chance = product of separate chances	0.00034		0.30

Behavior of multifactorial traits in families

Some traits are not determined predominantly by one gene (or a pair of genes at a single locus) but are determined by a considerable number of collaborating genes, each with rather minor effects. *Polygenic* is one designation for such traits. *Multifactorial* is used interchangeably by many geneticists, but may have a worthwhile separate significance since it takes into account the facts that both genetic and nongenetic factors are involved and that each is multiple. Multifactorial traits are usually of a type that is measured; unlike discontinuous traits, no black-or-white, yes-or-no, affected-or-unaffected classification of multifactorial traits is possible except by artificial and arbitrary designation or unless, as is discussed later, a threshold phenomenon occurs. Because of this characteristic, multifactorial traits are sometimes referred to as *quantitative traits*. Classic examples in man are intelligence and stature. Blood pressure, refractive index of the eye, dermatoglyphic ridge counts, and many others also qualify as multifactorial traits. In fact, because of the superficial level of phenotype analysis with present methods of study, multifactorial traits are far more numerous than monogenic ones.

Resemblance among relatives is a useful and important approach for the study of polygenic traits in man. In 1918 R. A. Fisher demonstrated that the findings of the early biometricians do not contradict Mendelian theory but are in full harmony with it and, in fact, can be rationally explained only in terms of Mendelism. He showed that the expected degree of resemblance among relatives, given polygenic inheritance and certain assumptions, is a simple mathematical expression. The regressions of child on parent, or parent on child, or sib on sib, or that of a more remote relative on the proband are equal to the number of genes in common. The expression *genes in common* refers to those genes derived from a common ancestor. The proportion of genes in common, and therefore the regression (Galton's term), for a number of relationships is shown in Table 6.10. The reader has already been introduced to this concept under a different name, the coefficient of relationship, symbolized by r (p. 104).

Table 6.10. Proportion of genes in common.

RELATIONSHIP TO PROBAND	PROPORTION OF GENES IN COMMON
Parent, child, sib	$\frac{1}{2}$
Monozygotic twin	1
Dizygotic twin	$\frac{1}{2}$
Grandparent, grandchild, uncle, aunt, nephew, niece, half sib	$\frac{1}{4}$
First cousin	$\frac{1}{8}$
Second cousin	$\frac{1}{32}$

The correlation coefficient is equivalent to the regression when two regressions, such as child-on-parent and parent-on-child, are equal. Since the mutual regressions are the same in each of the examples shown in Table 6.10, the correlation coefficients are equivalent to the regressions. (The correlation coefficient is the square root of the product of the two regressions, i.e., the regression of the first value on the second and the regression of the second value on the first: $\sqrt{r_1 \times r_2}$.)

The conditions under which the theoretical values for intrafamilial resemblances are realized are: (1) that inheritance alone is involved,

Fig. 6.11. Examples of three basic types of fingerprint patterns illustrating how ridge counts are made. (a) Arch (no triradius). The ridge count is zero. (b) Loop (one triradius, on the left where three ridges meet). A line has been drawn from the point of the triradius to the center of the loop. The ridge count, 13 in this case, is the number of ridges cutting the line. (c) Whorl (two triradii). The total ridge count is 25. Redrawn from Holt, *Brit. Med. Bull.*, **17** (1961), 247.

(2) that the gene pairs do not display dominance or recessiveness, i.e., that the heterozygote is intermediate between the two homozygotes, and (3) that values for husband and wife are not correlated, that is, that mating is random and not assortative, as far as the trait under study is concerned.

Of all the quantitative traits that have been studied adequately, fingerprint ridge counts provide one of the best examples of agreement between the expected and observed results (see Fig. 6.11 and Table 6.11). The total number of ridges from all ten fingers is taken as the

Table 6.11. Intrafamilial correlations for ridge counts.

RELATIONSHIP	CORRELATION COEFFICIENT Observed	Theoretical
Parent-child	0.48	0.50
Mother-child	0.48 ± 0.04	0.50
Father-child	0.49 ± 0.04	0.50
Parent-parent	0.05 ± 0.07	0
Mid-parent-child	0.66 ± 0.03	0.70
Sib-sib	0.50 ± 0.04	0.50
Monozygotic twin-twin	0.95 ± 0.01	1.00
Dizygotic twin-twin	0.49 ± 0.08	0.50

quantitative trait for study. One great advantage is that the dermal ridges are determined rather early in fetal life with no change thereafter, so that no troublesome allowances for change with age are necessary. The frequency distribution for ridge counts in a population approaches a normal bell-shaped curve, as one would expect of a polygenic trait, and, as would probably be the case if a single gene pair were involved, the curve is unimodal, not bimodal.

Certain conditions are necessary for the simplest theoretical expectations to be realized. There is no assortative mating for ridge counts since the parent-parent correlation is essentially zero. Dominance effects can be tested by using the regression of child on mid-parent (the mean measurement of the two parents). The theoretical regression is 1, since all the child's genes come from the two parents and the mid-parent measurement should be an accurate mean estimate if there is no dominance. The opposite regression, mid-parent on child, is theoretically $\frac{1}{2}$ because only half the genes of the two parents are identical to those of the child. The correlation coefficient (defined on p. 109), is, then, $1/\sqrt{2}$, or 0.71. As Table 6.11 indicates, the observed value departs only moderately from that expected, and there is, therefore, little dominance effect.

Stature and intelligence are polygenic in their genetic determination but have complicating features because of assortative mating, dominance, and environmental factors.

References

Holt, S. B., "Quantitative Genetics of Fingerprint Patterns," *Brit. Med. Bull.*, *17* (1961), 247-50.

Li, C. C., *Human Genetics*. New York: McGraw-Hill Book Company, 1961.

Maynard-Smith, Sheila, Lionel S. Penrose, and C. A. B. Smith, *Mathematical Tables for Research Workers in Human Genetics*. Boston: Little, Brown & Co., 1962.

Roberts, J. A. F., "Multifactorial Inheritance in Relation to Human Traits," *Brit. Med. Bull.*, *17* (1961), 241-46.

Genes in Populations

The Hardy–Weinberg principle states that genotype frequencies remain constant from generation to generation unless certain specific disturbing factors are introduced. The factors that disturb the Hardy–Weinberg equilibrium are nonrandom (or assortative) mating, mutation, selection, drift, and gene flow.

It should be clear from study of the algebraic example in Table 6.1 that nonrandom mating (for example, homozygous recessive persons marrying only other homozygous recessive persons) will disturb the Hardy–Weinberg equilibrium and increase the proportion of homozygotes at the expense of heterozygotes.

Mutation

Mutation (e.g., from A to a, occurring during gametogenesis in the parent generation) will change at least slightly the genotype frequencies in the offspring generation. Mutation is a relatively rare event, but it nonetheless provides the raw material of evolution; it provides the basis on which selection, with the collaboration of other factors discussed here, molds the genetic constitution of the species.

The frequency of mutation—the mutation rate—can be estimated in man for some genes, although at best the estimates are only approximations. For dominant genes both direct and indirect methods are available.

The direct method involves ascertaining all cases of a given disorder and determining which of the cases are sporadic, that is, are born of two unaffected parents. The number of sporadic cases is the numerator of the expression for the frequency of mutant individuals; the denominator is the number of births in the period of study. For example, Mørch found 10 achondroplastic dwarfs in 94,075 births in an obstetrical hospital in Copenhagen. Of the 10 cases of achondroplasia, 8 were alleged to have had unaffected parents. The frequency of mutant persons was, then, 1 in about 12,000 births. Since two gametes formed each individual, and since the mutation could have occurred in either the paternal or the maternal gamete, it is necessary to multiply the denominator by 2 to obtain the mutation rate in terms of mutations per gamete per generation; thus, the estimated mutation rate becomes 1 in 24,000, or about 4×10^{-5}. The algebraic expression for the mutation rate (μ), given the number of sporadic cases (n) and the total number of births (N) is

$$\mu = \frac{n}{2N}$$

Several difficulties make the mutation rates determined by the method above no more than "guestimates." Illegitimacy, with the true father an affected person, introduces inaccuracy in the labeling of cases as sporadic. So also does mild expression of the gene in an affected parent such that both parents are considered unaffected. Furthermore, the condition under study may not be a single entity having all cases determined by a mutation at one locus. The phenotype may be an environmentally induced phenocopy. Genetic mimics, i.e., the same phenotype determined by mutation at more than one locus, may be involved; however, expressing the mutation rate in terms of gametes per generation, rather than in terms of loci, avoids this difficulty. Some of the apparently sporadic dominant cases may in fact be homozygotes for a simulating recessive disorder. In the example of achondroplastic dwarfism used above there is real reason to suspect that heterogeneity exists and that the estimate derived is too high. Finally, total ascertainment is difficult to achieve.

The indirect method is based on an assumption of equilibrium between mutation (which is adding mutant genes to the gene pool) and negative selection (which is removing the mutant genes from the pool). For social and biological reasons, achondroplastic dwarfs reproduce at a much reduced level as compared with the average. The reproductive fitness has been estimated at about .20, when the general average is 1.0. This means that achondroplastic dwarfs as a group have only one-fifth as many children as do normal people. Furthermore it means that $1 - .20$, or $.80$ of cases of achondroplasia in the next generation arise by new mutation. Mørch found 10 achondroplastic dwarfs in 94,000 births, and presumably 8 of these arose by new mutation. The 94,000 births represent 188,000 gametes; thus, a mutation rate of 8/188,000, or about 1 in 24,000 gametes per generation is calculated. The general expression is

$$\mu = \frac{(1 - f)n}{2N}$$

where f is relative fitness, n is the number of cases, and N is the total number of births.

The indirect method has some of the same difficulties as the direct method, e.g., the uncertainty of complete ascertainment and of homogeneity of the phenotype. In addition, it is often difficult to be confident of the estimate of fitness, especially in regard to the average number of children in the general population, a value that is used for comparison. If the average number of children of unaffected sibs of cases is used, errors may arise since the normal members of the family may have either more or fewer children for reasons related to the presence of the particular gene in the family.

The indirect method can be used for estimating the mutation rate for X-linked traits, most of which are recessive in the female. Only affected males are ascertained; in the male the mutant allele behaves as though it were dominant. The denominator is multiplied by 3 rather than by 2 to arrive at the estimate per gamete, since the mutation can occur in either gamete of the female or in the X-bearing gamete of the male. Another difficulty in estimating the mutation rate of X-borne genes is deciding whether the mutation in a sporadically-affected male occurred in a gamete of his mother or whether it occurred in a gamete of one of her parents, or even earlier ancestors, and by chance escaped previous detection.

Mutation rates have been estimated for a considerable number of rare pathologic traits of man. Most estimates are of the order of 10^{-5}, that is, 1 in 100,000 gametes per generation.

For autosomal recessive traits, only the indirect method is applicable. Again the question is what mutation rate is necessary to maintain equilibrium (constant gene frequency) in the face of a certain loss of genes through negative selection. Again most of the difficulties enumerated earlier are encountered; in addition, it is very likely that the given recessive gene in the heterozygous state is not entirely neutral but has either a deleterious or an advantageous effect on reproductive fitness. If the heterozygote is at an advantage a lower mutation rate suffices to replace the genes lost in the homozygote. This selective effect in the heterozygote is difficult to measure, however.

Cystic fibrosis of the pancreas is the most frequent lethal simply inherited disease of childhood, occurring about once in every 3,000 white births in the United States; very few of the persons affected with it reproduce. The evidence for autosomal recessive inheritance of this disease is convincing. To maintain equilibrium between genes added by new mutation and genes lost by early death of homozygotes, a mutation rate of 1 in 1,500 gametes per generation is required. Such an unprecedented estimate is regarded with suspicion, and alternative possibilities are sought. One such possibility is the existence of many loci at any one of which mutation can result in the same phenotype. But even if there are 10 such loci, an average mutation rate of about 1 in 15,000 would be required. A more likely possibility is that the heterozygote enjoys an advantage over the homozygous normal, but as yet there is no evidence that the heterozygote is indeed at an advantage and no proven mechanism by which the heterozygote might be at an advantage.

Another question of interest is whether mutation occurs with equal frequency in spermatogenesis and oögenesis. The time course and other aspects of gametogenesis differ noticeably in the two sexes (see Chapter 2); hence vulnerability to mutation might also differ. In humans the relative frequency of mutation in the male and female can be estimated by an analysis of X-linked traits. If the mutation rate is higher in the female, a disproportionate number of cases in a series will be sporadic, since only the X chromosome given to the son by the mother carries the mutation. If the mutation rate is higher in spermatogenesis, a disproportionate number of cases will be of the familial type, since the one X chromosome of the male bearing the mutation will be transmitted to a daughter who, as a carrier, may have multiple affected sons. Data on hemophilia and on X-linked muscular dystrophy give no clear evidence of a sex difference in mutation rate.

There is evidence that the age of the parent makes a difference in mutation rate. In achondroplastic dwarfism and in certain other conditions the fathers of sporadic cases (that presumably resulted from new mutation) are appreciably older than the average. Correlation of the secondary sex ratio with the age of the maternal grandfather at conception of the mother has been proposed as an approach for determining the effect of age on mutation rate. The secondary sex ratio (ratio at birth) is about 106 males to 100 females. If X-linked recessive mutations, some of them lethal *in utero*, occur with increased frequency in older men, then these might be transmitted to their daughters and segregate in their grandsons, producing a reduction in the ratio.

It is quite certain that most persons, and perhaps all people, carry at least one or two highly deleterious "recessive genes" in the heterozygous state. This follows directly from the calculation of the frequency of heterozygotes of the numerous autosomal recessive disorders that are known, and is confirmed by investigations of the results of consanguineous marriages. Such studies have led to the concept of "lethal equivalents." For example, it is estimated that man carries from 3 to 8 lethal equivalents—that is, many genes, each with slightly deleterious effects, which are the equivalent of 3 to 8 recessive genes that if in the homozygous state would result in death before reproduction.

Causes of mutation

Definable causes of an increased mutation rate are ionizing radiation, chemicals, and heat.

Mutations in the general sense are of two types: point mutations and gross chromosomal changes. The latter type is discussed on page 23. The fact that gross chromosomal aberrations have been observed in man following exposure to ionizing radiation and nitrogen mustard is strong evidence that these agents also produce point mutations.

It has been estimated that the total gonadal dosage of X ray (mainly diagnostic) received by persons in the United States before completion of the reproductive span averages 3.0 r (roentgens) and is probably not less than 2.0 r. Fallout from the testing of weapons is approximately 0.1 r. Awareness of the genetic and other risks involved has led to intense surveillance on the part of the medical and paramedical professions, and elimination of many diagnostic procedures, such as fluoroscopy and X rays for pelvic size in pregnant women, that represented heavy exposures.

The mutagenic effect of many chemicals has been proved in other species. One of these chemicals, nitrogen mustard (or related substances), is used in the treatment of certain malignant neoplastic diseases of man. Their use is, of course, justified without particular concern for the mutagenic risks because of the seriousness of the disease being treated. Furthermore, these individuals usually do not have any children after such treatment. Many other chemicals in our food or medical therapeutic armamentarium have mutagenic effects in other species; their effects in man, however, have not been demonstrated. Caffeine (trimethylxanthine) and theobromine (dimethylxanthine) are structurally related to adenine and guanine, two of the DNA four bases that by various combinations, probably in triplets, encode the genetic information. Evidence for a mutagenic effect of caffeine is available in *Escherichia coli* and in *Drosophila melanogaster;* however, experiments in mice have thus far failed to demonstrate a mutagenic effect.

Heat increases the "spontaneous" mutation rate. Measurements of scrotal temperature in men wearing pants and nude showed an appreciably higher temperature in the former case. Calculations based on the temperature effect on mutation rate suggest that the wearing of trousers may be an important factor; some have recommended that kilts would be less mutagenic. (Note that this phenomenon is not to be confused with that of "mutator genes"!)

Selection

Selection is another factor that disturbs the Hardy–Weinberg equilibrium by resulting in gene frequencies in the offspring generation different from those in the parent generation. Fitness, in the biological or Darwinian sense, is defined in terms of the contribution made to the genes of the succeeding generation. Selection is differential fitness according to the genotype of the organism, and may operate on both the haploid gamete and the diploid organism. It can furthermore have its effects at any stage from the zygote to the adult individual who has not yet completed the reproductive period. The critical matter is whether reproduction occurs so that the gene is represented in the succeeding generation.

For the purposes of analysis, selection (and its complementary parameter, fitness) can be divided into survivance selection (focusing on the factors that determine whether the organism survives to the time of reproduction) and reproductive selection (focusing on the factors that determine efficiency of reproduction).

Figure 7.1a shows the types of families one would expect to find in a collection of families with at least one member affected by an autosomal dominant trait, bearers of which have a fitness half that of the general population—i.e., on the average affected persons have only half as many children as do unaffected persons. Assuming equilibrium, one concludes that about half the families will have but one case resulting from new mutation that balances the loss of the mutant gene through negative selection (reduced fitness). Figure 7.1b shows the types of families one would expect in a collection of families ascertained through a male affected by a rare X-linked recessive trait if the males never reproduce and if the fitness of carrier females is no different from that of the general population.

R. A. Fisher pointed out that a dominant mutation that has no selective advantage or disadvantage still has a better-than-1-per-cent chance of survival after 127 generations. Perhaps the longest documented survival of a dominant gene in man is the case of transmission through at least fourteen generations of the gene for symphalangism, a fusion of the proximal and middle phalanges of the fingers.

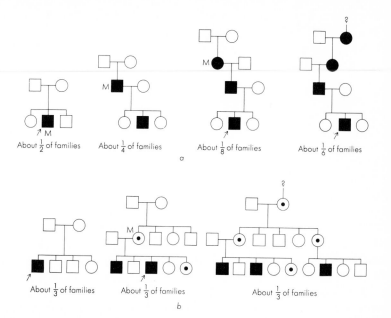

Fig. 7.1. (*a*) Types of pedigrees in a collection of families with at least one member affected by an autosomal dominant trait that has a fitness of $\frac{1}{2}$. (*b*) Types of pedigrees in a collection of families with at least one male affected by an X-linked recessive trait that has a fitness of zero. After Carter, *Human Heredity* (Penguin, 1962).

In heterozygotes, gametes carrying one allele may be produced in preference to those carrying the other, so-called meiotic drive. Gametes carrying a particular gene may be at an advantage or disadvantage relative to those carrying an allele. Some evidence concerning the occurrence of these phenomena in man has become available in recent years.

The zygote or fetus of a particular genotype may likewise fare better or worse than those of other genotypes. Fetuses heterozygous for Rhesus or some other blood groups are, on the average, at a disadvantage because of the ill effects of materno-fetal incompatibility. Any of the genes causing disorders or predisposition to disorders that lead to death in the years before reproduction obviously place their bearer at a strong selective disadvantage.

One of the clearest examples of selective advantage of a particular genotype in a particular environment is the now familiar one of sickling. The heterozygote enjoys an advantage in a malarious environment. There are at least four indications that malaria has played this role in selection. (1) Geographic distributions of malaria and of high gene *S* frequency showed a close correlation in Africa. (2) Counts of malarial parasites in the blood are lower in *Hb SA* persons than in *Hb AA* persons. (3) *Hb SA* persons are probably more susceptible than *Hb AA* persons to experimental malaria. (4) Mortality from cerebral malaria is less in *Hb SA* persons than in *Hb AA* persons. Only item 4 represents direct evidence of selection.

The mechanism of this advantage is not known with certainty. Possibly parasitized red cells become sickled and because of their misshape are removed from the circulation and disposed of more rapidly than would otherwise occur. This mechanism is probably especially important in the early years of life before immunization has had time to develop to the fullest. Pregnant mothers may also be less likely to get the malarial lesions of the placenta that cause abortion, again because the parasitized red cells are removed from the circulation. Whatever the mechanism of the advantage, it prevails only in the face of the malignant form (the falciparum type) of malaria. Hemoglobin C also confers an advantage with reference to malaria. Since Hb C disease (the homozygous state) is not as virulent a disease as Hb S disease, selection against the homozygote is not as rigorous, and less selective advantage on the part of the heterozygote is required to maintain relatively high gene frequencies.

In a nonmalarious environment the sickle heterozygote is actually at a disadvantage. Rupture of the spleen is, for example, likely to occur when the *SA* individual goes to a high altitude in airplane flight. This illustrates an important point: a genotype advantageous in one environment may be quite disadvantageous in another.

The question is often raised as to whether selection has not been greatly relaxed today as compared with some centuries ago. Certainly the efforts of modern medicine today keep alive individuals who, in an earlier and more precarious setting, would have been easy prey. Undoubtedly the negative selection acting on the gene or genes responsible for conditions such as diabetes, cleft palate, cataract, and retinoblastoma has been appreciably relaxed. Conversely, however, unknown selective factors that, operating in the past, effected a present high frequency of diabetes genes may no longer be at work.

At any rate, much opportunity for selection remains today, and in some ways selection pressure is stronger than in the past. It is estimated that close to half of all zygotes never reproduce. About 15 per cent are lost before birth, 3 per cent are stillborn, 2 per cent die in the neonatal period, 3 per cent die before maturity, 20 per cent never marry, and 10 per cent of those who marry remain childless. Thus, there is considerable room for selection. Genotypic differences that favor survival to reproduction at any of these stages will enjoy an advantage.

The advantage or disadvantage in the race for reproduction can be a rather minor one; yet when applied to large groups of people, and when operating over many generations, the impact on the genetic constitution of man is great. For example, in the case of cystic fibrosis that was cited earlier, an advantage of the heterozygote of only about 1 per cent would suffice to maintain the high gene frequency without any mutation. (A 1 per cent advantage means that the heterozygotes as a group have 1 per cent more children than the homozygous normals.) In part this is due to the large size of the heterozygous population.

The significance of association (e.g., blood-group-and-disease association) is the influence it may have had on the genetic constitution of man through selection. It is difficult to believe that the impressive associations between peptic ulcer and blood group O and between peptic ulcer and nonsecretion have had much effect on the world-wide distribution of ABO blood groups. Peptic ulcer, a disease of adulthood, probably does not interfere appreciably with reproduction. On the other hand, it has been suggested that differences in ABO blood type may be related to resistance to infectious diseases such as smallpox and plague, which have been terribly devastating in the past, and that ABO frequencies observed today are the result of selection working through this mechanism. The smallpox virus may bear antigenic similarity to blood group A antigen; persons of blood group B or O, having natural antibody against blood group A, may be more resistant to smallpox. A similar line of reasoning has been applied to plague, the causative organism of which (*Pasteurella pestis*) bears antigenic similarities to H blood-group substance. Correlations of ABO blood-group frequencies with known epidemics of the past and contemporary observations on the severity and outcome of smallpox and plague according to blood type are the main approaches for testing this attractive hypothesis.

Geneticists today do not suppose that any trait, e.g., the blood groups, is completely neutral as far as selection is concerned. Selection is thought to be the main reason for differences in gene frequencies in different populations, although drift and gene flow are also important; however, their relative importance is sometimes difficult to evaluate.

Tuberculosis is to a considerable extent a disease of urbanization. It killed large numbers of Europeans in past centuries but had already begun to decline sharply before the advent of effective drugs. Improved hygiene does not adequately account for this decline. A more likely explanation is the rise of more resistant stock through natural selection. The pronounced vulnerability of some groups, such as the Eskimos, American Indians, and Negroes who have not passed through this screen of selection, supports this assertion. The effective treatment of tuberculosis will presumably result in a loss of genetic resistance because of relaxation of selection. However, man will be fitter in other respects. If the genes for resistance to tuberculosis had caused increased fitness in the absence of tuberculosis, then they would have already become frequent in populations. Thus, in the absence of tuberculosis they either make for reduced fitness or are relatively neutral. At any rate, it follows that the drug treatment of tuberculosis is not dysgenic and is probably eugenic.

Drift

Drift, originally called random genetic drift by Sewall Wright, who developed the concept, occurs in small populations or isolates that form for geographic, religious, or social reasons. Although isolates have all but disappeared today because of improved means of transportation and communication, increase in the world's population, and urbanization, man was a relatively rare mammal that existed in small groups, in the not so remote past.

In statistics, the standard deviation in small experiments is greater than in large experiments. If a small number of animals has been tested in an experiment, the "confidence limits" on the value determined as the average for the variable tested are much wider than if a large number of animals is used. Drift is a comparable matter: in small populations the frequency of one gene may by chance rise to high proportions. In a small religious isolate, the Dunkers of Pennsylvania, the frequency of the genes for blood groups A, B, and O were found to be quite different from those of the parent population in Germany from which the Dunkers were derived. Effects of this type might have been stronger in earlier times when the total human population of the earth was small and men lived in small groups, especially on islands or in other geographically isolated areas.

The founder effect is an example of drift. If an unpopulated area was colonized by a few married couples, by chance differing widely from the average of the parent population in the genes they carry, e.g., for various blood groups, the descendant population might differ markedly from the parent population.

An example of founder effect is the unprecedented frequency in the Old Order Amish of Lancaster County, Pennsylvania, of the gene which in homozygous state causes a particular form of dwarfism accompanied by extra fingers (polydactyly). Almost all 8,000 persons in this isolate include among their ancestors three couples who came to America before 1770. Although dwarfism-polydactyly, a simple recessive, is so rare that scarcely more than 50 cases have hitherto been reported in the medical literature, about 55 definite cases have been found among the Amish of Lancaster County; about 13 per cent of persons in this group are heterozygous for the gene. By chance one of the "founders" must have been a carrier of this gene, which is very rare in the general population. Amish groups elsewhere than in Pennsylvania, for example, Ohio and Indiana, had other founding fathers and do not have this abnormality.

It is often difficult to evaluate the relative importance of selection and drift in determining gene frequencies observed today. For example, there is a high frequency of blood group O (almost 100 per cent) in South American and many North American Indians, whereas Oriental peoples from whom they were derived have a rather low frequency of blood group O. Whether the shift to high O in American Indians resulted from selection or from drift is unknown. Drift probably was responsible for certain atypical frequencies such as the high frequency of blood group A (up to 80 per cent) in Blackfoot and Blood Indians, as compared with 2 per cent in the Ute Indians.

Gene flow

Gene flow is the change in the genetic constitution of populations as a result of addition of new genes by migration, contact with invading armies, and miscegenation. Selective migration can influence the make-up of both the donor and the recipient population.

The distribution of ABO blood groups illustrates the influence of migration on genetic constitution. In Great Britain there is a cline from high A-gene frequency in the south of England to high O-gene frequency in Scotland (Fig. 7.2a). This cline is thought to be due to the progressive northward retreat of aboriginal peoples with high O frequency before the pressures of more recent immigrants with high A frequency from the Continent. In Ireland, too, the varying mixtures of the original Irish on the one hand and the Norman and English invaders on the other are shown by the cline from high O frequency in the west to relatively high A frequency in the east of the island.

A similar cline across Asia and Europe from high B and low A frequencies in the East and to low B and high A frequencies in the West (Fig. 7.2b) has been ascribed to effects of the Tartar-Mongol invasions of 500-1500 A.D. It is found that descendants of refugees who fled into the mountain strongholds of the Caucasus have low blood-group B frequency, and retain the social and linguistic traits of their forebears.

Africans indigenous to the area south of the Sahara have certain blood-group peculiarities that distinguish them from other peoples. One of these features is high Rh type cDe (R_0). The frequencies of

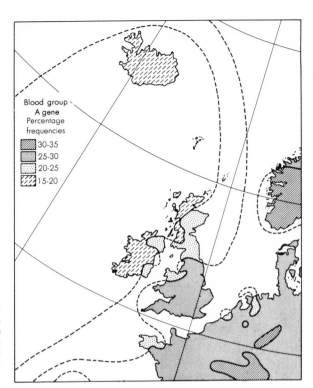

Blood group
A gene
Percentage
frequencies

30-35
25-30
20-25
15-20

Fig. 7.2. (a, right) Cline for blood group A gene in United Kingdom, Ireland, and Iceland. (b, below) Cline for blood group B gene on Eurasian continent. Redrawn from Mourant, et al., The ABO Blood Groups (Blackwell Scientific Publications, 1958).

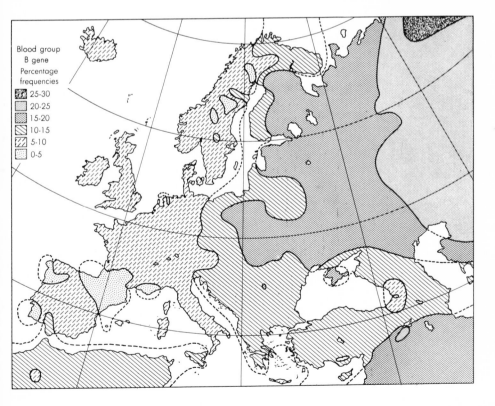

Blood group
B gene
Percentage
frequencies

25-30
20-25
15-20
10-15
5-10
0-5

the blood-group genes seem relatively stable, thus permitting an estimate of the degree of miscegenation of Caucasians and Africans in the United States. For social reasons gene flow has been almost exclusively from Caucasian to African. Using the Rhesus blood group, one arrives at an estimate that the American Negro is about 30 per cent Caucasian, i.e., about 30 per cent of the total gene pool carried by American Negroes is of Caucasian contribution. Using other polymorphisms with strikingly different frequencies in Africans and Europeans, almost identical estimates of white-Negro admixture have been obtained.

Terms

Certain terms used in population genetics must be clearly defined. *Incidence* and *prevalence* have acquired rather specific meanings, mainly in studies of the epidemiology of infectious diseases. *Incidence* refers to the number of new cases that develop in a certain period of time. In human genetics it would be appropriate to speak of the incidence of Mongoloid idiocy as 1 in 500 births since a period of time, that required for 500 births to occur, is implicit. *Prevalence* refers to frequency of "cases" found in a population at any one point in time. It is appropriate to speak of the prevalence of Mongoloid idiocy in a given population in which total ascertainment has been achieved. No period of time is implied; the enumeration is at one point in time. The main confusion involves the term *incidence*. To avoid such confusion the term *frequency* has much to recommend it. It should, however, be made clear whether phenotype frequency or gene frequency is referred to.

Reference

Glass, Bentley, "Genetic Changes in Populations, Especially Those Due to Gene Flow and Genetic Drift," *Advan. Genet., 6* (1954), 95-139.

Eight

Genes and Evolution

Separation of a discussion of "genes and evolution" from "genes in populations" is entirely arbitrary. Evolution in simplest terms is the change in the genetic constitution of an organism. The important factors in evolution—those influencing gene frequencies—were discussed in the preceding chapter. Several additional topics, however, are worthy of discussion.

R. A. Fisher pointed out that grave genetic defects have not always been recessive to the wild type as now seems to be the case for a majority of conditions. He postulated that through the accumulation of genetic modifiers the effects of genes in the heterozygote were gradually mollified to the point that their action is recognizable only, or almost only, in the homozygote. It is not difficult to imagine that when a deleterious dominant mutation was occurring repeatedly, modifying genes that reduced the deleterious effects would be favored in selection. Fisher originated the expression "the evolution of dominance" for this phenomenon.

Evolution of the genetic material itself can be deduced from the nature of certain proteins of related structure. Unequal crossing over between homologous chromosomes and subsequent divergence through independent mutation of the duplicate loci is thought to be a frequent mechanism. This phenomenon probably accounts for the

125

findings in the hemoglobins. The locus responsible for the synthesis of delta chains of hemoglobin A_2 is very closely linked to the locus determining beta chains of hemoglobin A, and there are close chemical similarities between the β-polypeptide chain and the δ-polypeptide chain. In fact they differ by only 8 amino acids. Hence it is logical to assume that gene duplication and divergent mutation have occurred.

Gene duplication is a mechanism that permits more rapid and more extensive evolution of proteins than can be achieved by mutation alone. Furthermore, it has the advantage that the parent protein, with any beneficial effects it may have, need not be lost.

Unequal crossing over may be intragenic rather than intergenic with the production of a new allele that has some characteristics of one gene and other characteristics of another. The close study of amino acid sequences of certain proteins of man has turned up several instances where this has probably happened.

Parenthetically, it should be noted that the analysis of protein structure is a powerful, although indirect, method for fine-structure genetic analysis in man—genetic analysis at the intragenic level. Intragenic inversions, deletions, shifts, and other changes can, at least theoretically, be identified by this method.

Deductions on the evolution of the several polypeptide chains of the hemoglobins can be made from chemical homologies, i.e., the similarities and dissimilarities in amino acid sequence. Hemoglobin probably arose from a relatively simple myoglobin-like protein with one polypeptide chain. The loci determining alpha and beta chains must have diverged from the primordial locus in the remote past. The delta locus probably evolved from the beta locus through gene duplication; evidence for this relatively recent evolution is provided by the facts that Hb A_2 occurs only in primates, that there is about 95 per cent amino acid homology between the delta and beta chains, and that the delta and beta loci are closely linked. The gamma locus appears to have originated at an intermediate stage. These relationships are schematized in Fig. 8.1.

At the chromosome level as well as at the protein level, the course of evolution can be traced by the study of homologies. As is indicated in Fig. 8.2 there are some striking similarities between the karyotype of man and that of his rather close relative, the gorilla. There is reason to think that homologous chromosomes, e.g., the X chromosome of gorilla and man, may have similar genetic content. Linkage and other methods for genetic analysis in man are crude and laborious. Based on the reasonable hypothesis of homology, genetic analysis in man may be furthered by study in other species in which experimental matings are possible.

The mechanisms leading to balanced polymorphism, such as the

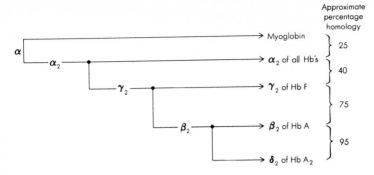

Fig. 8.1. The evolution of the human oxygen-transporting and oxygen-storing proteins, hemoglobin and myoglobin. Based on Ingram, *Federation Proc.*, 21 (1962), 1053-57.

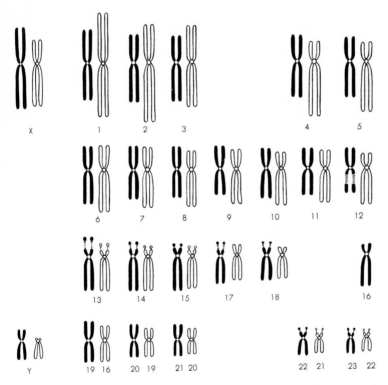

Fig. 8.2. A comparison of the karyotype of the gorilla (black figures) with that of man (open figures). The gorilla has 48 chromosomes. After Hamerton, *et al.*, *Nature*, *192* (1961), 225. (Hamilton now concludes that the x chromosome of the gorilla is the 5th or 6th in size, not the largest as shown here.)

relatively high frequency of color blindness in many human populations, are not clearly understood. One plausible explanation for this particular polymorphism is that in a society of hunters the color-blind man was less confused by the camouflaging mimicry that evolved in many animals as a protection against its predators. An opposite view is that color blindness was a disadvantageous trait in a hunting society and that selection against the trait has been relaxed in recent millenniums. The proponents of this hypothesis point to the low frequency of color blindness in aboriginal peoples.

We have seen how a "pathological gene," that for sickle hemoglobin, may be advantageous in some environmental circumstances. Myopia (nearsightedness), a polygenic trait, may have been advantageous in early societies. The young man incapable of hunting because of the visual defect may have been forced into intellectual pursuits that in the long run were more advantageous to society. Shocking as the notion may seem, even death may have a selective advantage: in primitive societies aged persons no longer capable of reproduction or of productive labor are a burden.

Races

Races of man are distinguished by their possession of aggregates of different genes, or the same genes in different frequencies, or both. There are, however, numerous genetic similarities between races, making classification difficult. In fact, no classification satisfactory to all anthropologists has been devised. The standard classification that is supported by differences in blood group frequencies is:

(1) European (Caucasoid)
(2) African (Negroid)
(3) Asiatic (Mongoloid)
(4) American Indian
(5) Australoid

A more elaborate classification with its basis in both geography and physical traits is:

(1) Amerindian
(2) Polynesian—islands of eastern Pacific, New Zealand to Hawaii and Easter Island
(3) Micronesian—islands of western Pacific, from Guam to Marshall and Gilbert Islands
(4) Melanesian—islands of western Pacific, from New Guinea to New Caledonia and Fiji
(5) Australian
(6) Asiatic
(7) Indian—populations of the subcontinent of India
(8) European
(9) African

Even finer classifications—into as many as 34 races—have been suggested. These classifications list, for example, the Bantu, Pigmy, North

American Colored, Eskimo, and others as separate races. All races are Mendelian populations that change in time through the influences of the factors discussed earlier. Some of the racial groups in the more detailed classifications have arisen in the last 400 years or less, e.g., the North American Colored and the Neo-Hawaiian.

At any rate, man is all one species with no chromosomal differences between the various races and with free interbreeding possible. New subraces may develop in the future through intermixture, but new major races are not likely to evolve unless man is widely scattered into small groups by a nuclear war or other form of cataclysm.

Thus far, studies have failed to reveal evidence for hybrid vigor in interracial crosses in man, but this is perhaps not surprising since man is already extensively outbred.

References

Chu, E. H. Y., and M. A. Bender, "Cytogenetics of the Primates and Primate Evolution," *Ann. N.Y. Acad. Sci.*, *102* (1962), 253-66.

Coon, Carleton S., *The Story of Man*, 2nd ed. New York: Alfred A. Knopf, Inc., 1962.

————, *The Origin of Races*. New York: Alfred A. Knopf, Inc., 1962.

Dobzhansky, Theodosius, *Mankind Evolving: The Evolution of the Human Species*. New Haven: Yale University Press, 1962.

Hamerton, John L., *et. al.* "Somatic Chromosomes of the Gorilla," *Nature*, *192* (1961), 225-28.

Hoagland, Hudson, and R. W. Burhoe, eds., *Evolution and Man's Progress*. New York: Columbia University Press, 1962.

Huntington, Ellsworth, *Mainsprings of Civilization*. New York: John Wiley and Sons, Inc., 1945.

Ingram, Vernon M., *The Hemoglobins in Genetics and Evolution*. New York: Columbia University Press, 1963.

$\bigwedge ine$

Genes and Disease

Medical genetics is the aspect of human genetics that is concerned with the relationship between heredity and disease.

The mutant gene should be viewed as an etiological agent in disease, comparable to a bacterium or a virus. One sometimes hears that the aim of a particular research program is to discover the *cause* of hereditary muscular dystrophy. Actually the cause has long been known. The cause of muscular dystrophy is a mutant gene (or several mutant genes, since several forms of hereditary muscular dystrophy can be distinguished). What is sought in such research are the mechanisms, the nature of the gene-determined biochemical defect in each form of muscular dystrophy.

The practice of medicine resolves itself mainly into seeking the answers to three questions: What is wrong? (Diagnosis); What is going to happen? (Prognosis); and What can be done? (Treatment). (In addition it is the scientific and social responsibility of the physician to keep in mind a fourth question: Why did it happen?) Diagnosis, prognosis, and treatment provide a useful framework within which to discuss the role of genetics in the practice of medicine.

Diagnosis

In diagnosis genetic knowledge is useful in the recognition of grave internal disease from external clues that are part of a hereditary single-gene syndrome (see p. 59). Also, early manifestations or mild expression (*forme fruste*) of hereditary disease can often be recognized through knowledge of the family history and the usual familial pattern of the genetic disorder in question.

In some conditions in which the exact mode of inheritance is not yet known, e.g., diabetes mellitus, the knowledge that the disorder runs in families and that the particular family in question has several members affected can at least serve the useful function of arousing suspicion that this disorder of carbohydrate metabolism is the basis for otherwise unexplained symptoms in the patient. If the parents of a patient are related (a rare occurrence in this country at present) the pediatrician may be inclined more strongly toward the possibility of an autosomal recessive disorder as the basis of the child's symptoms.

Prognosis

Prognosis in medical genetics has features that distinguish it from prognosis in other fields of medicine. Frequently the question, "What is going to happen?" applies to the unborn offspring of the persons seeking advice, and not to that person himself. Once a child is born with a hereditary disorder, the parents often wonder what the risk is that another child will be similarly affected.

In the case of many conditions, most of them individually rare, it is possible to state the genetic risk in terms of rather precise probabilities. For example, once a child affected by a clearly autosomal recessive disorder has been born of unaffected parents the risk to any child subsequently born is, of course, one in four. Even if three or more children, all affected, have been born, the risk is still one in four. "Chance has no memory." For any child of a person affected by an autosomal dominant disorder (that has reasonably complete penetrance) the risk is one in two.

In the case of X-linked disorders (most behave as recessives), the problems of genetic counselling are somewhat different. What, for example, is the risk that a sister of a hemophiliac will have a hemophilic son? The risk in such a case varies greatly, depending on whether the hemophilic brother inherited his disease from a carrier mother or whether his disease arose through a new mutation in the X chromosome contributed by his mother. If there are affected maternal uncles, then the answer to the question is one in four. The risk of the sister being a carrier is one in two and the risk of her having a hemophilic son if she is a carrier is again one in two; the risk to a son is, then, the product, one in four.

Obviously the ability to identify persons heterozygous for a "recessive gene," either X-linked or autosomal, would be of great value in genetic counselling. The methods presently available give, for most conditions, an imperfect separation between the heterozygote and the normal homozygote. If the test—for serum enzymes in the case of the sister of a boy with X-linked muscular dystrophy, or for antihemophilic globulin in the case of the sister of a hemophiliac—yields a value well outside the normal range, then it is possible to state with considerable certainty that the person is a carrier. However, if the value is in the normal range, one cannot be confident that the person is not a carrier.

In many conditions, e.g., congenital malformations such as harelip, cleft palate, and congenital heart disease, the role of genetic factors is sufficiently unclear that genetic risks can be estimated only in empiric terms. For example, in a collection of families with normal parents and a single child with harelip, a frequency of 4 per cent of harelip may have been found among offspring born subsequent to the affected child. If one parent is also affected, the risk is increased, and so on. Empiric-risk figures undoubtedly exaggerate the risk in some families and underestimate it in others. In this situation, as in so many others in medical genetics, the likelihood of heterogeneity must be kept in mind. One looks for objective features that may make it possible to arrive at a more precise estimate of the genetic risk in some cases. There are, for example, rare forms of cleft palate that have simple Mendelian inheritance. Although the genetics of these congenital malformations is complex and information inprecise, the risk of recurrence is low; the more complex the genetics, the lower the risk.

Often genetic counselling affords relief from worries rather than inciting or aggravating anguish. Usually the person seeking genetic counselling thinks the risk is greater than it really is. Persons in hemophilic families may be worried that they can have affected children and are likely to be relieved if pedigree analysis demonstrates that it is unlikely or completely impossible for them to transmit the disorder; the nonhemophilic brother of a hemophiliac cannot transmit hemophilia to his descendants, but he may not know this. A man with pseudoxanthoma elasticum (failing vision and severe disease of blood vessels) inherited as an autosomal recessive is relieved to learn that the risk is negligible that his children by an unrelated wife will be affected.

Another aspect of genetic prognostication is illustrated by Huntington's chorea, which is a neurologic disorder in which the age of onset of manifestations (abnormal movements and eventual dementia) may vary from the first to the seventh decade. A member of a family with multiple persons affected by this disorder in an autosomal dominant pattern may ask what the risk is that he carries the gene and that manifestations of the disorder will appear later in his life? Unfortunately there are no foolproof early signs of the disease to help in answering the question. A tentative answer is illustrated by this example: A 28-year-old man without signs of this disease has an unaffected father aged 58 years, and a paternal grandmother who died at 70 years of age of Huntington's chorea. The risk of the young man's developing the disease is dependent on whether the father carries the gene or not. The probability that the father is free of the gene can be estimated from the proportion of cases that are manifest by age 58. Over 95 per cent of cases are in fact identified by age 58. The a priori probability of the father's being affected is $\frac{1}{2}$. With the further consideration that he has not developed disease by age 58, the probability becomes $<.05 \times 0.50$, or less than 2.5 per cent. The probability of the father transmitting the gene to his son is again $\frac{1}{2}$. Thus, the risk of the 28-year-old son developing Huntington's chorea is of the order of 1 per cent.

Useful assistance can be provided in predicting the course of the disease in a person who already has symptoms if, in a given family, both the similarity and the range of variability in the manifestation of a mutant gene are taken into account. For example, in different families the form of retinal degeneration called retinitis pigmentosa shows differences in the rate at which the disorder progresses to blindness.

Treatment

Treatment in genetic disease is not as hopeless as it may seem. There is, of course, a difference between treatment and cure; cure is not now possible unless the surgical correction of genetically determined abnormalities can be considered as a cure. Opportunities for treatment in genetic disease arise in part from the fact that almost all disease is at least to some extent the result of collaboration of environmental and genetic etiologic factors (see p. 57).

There are several forms of therapy for genetic diseases:

(1) Elimination diets. In galactosemia and phenylketonuria, galactose and phenylalanine, respectively, cannot be metabolized properly; their accumulation results in pathologic symptoms. Elimination of galactose and phenylalanine from the diet at an early stage can prevent irreversible damage.

(2) Dietary supplementation. In oroticaciduria there is a genetic defect in the synthesis of uridylic acid and cytidylic acid, both essential to normal pyrimidine metabolism. If uracil and cytosine are taken

orally in adequate amounts, no manifestations of the enzyme defect will develop. Avitaminoses and deficiencies of essential amino acids are not viewed as primarily genetic disorders since all human beings seem to require these dietary elements. However, as compared with some other mammalian species, man has a genetic defect in vitamin C synthesis; "treatment" of this genetic defect is dietary consumption of vitamin C.

(3) Avoidance of drugs. Certain antimalarial and other drugs and also the fava bean precipitate hemolysis in persons with the X-linked genetic deficiency of erythrocyte glucose-6-phosphate dehydrogenase. Clearly, preventive treatment consists of avoiding the offending agent.

(4) Elimination from the body. Hemochromatosis is a hereditary disorder in which, by some mechanism not yet clearly understood, iron accumulates in the body in very large amounts, producing severely deleterious effects on the heart, liver, and pancreas. An effective method for removing iron from the body is repeated venesection.

(5) Replacement of a missing gene product. The administration of antihemophilic globulin in hemophilia and of thyroid hormone in the several genetic defects of thyroid hormone synthesis are examples.

(6) Competitive inhibition. In oxalosis, because of a defect in the degradation of glyoxalate to CO_2 and H_2O, glyoxalate is converted in greatly excessive amounts to oxalate. The administration of sodium hydroxymethane sulfonate, which acts as a substrate for the same enzyme involved in the conversion of glyoxalate to oxalate, may be effective treatment.

(7) Replacement of defective tissue. Kidney transplantation in hereditary cystic disease of the kidney is a potentially feasible form of therapy, but the problems of tissue incompatibility must first be solved.

(8) Preventive therapy. Surgical removal of the colon in cases of hereditary polyposis of the colon, which is notoriously liable to develop cancer, is an example.

(9) Other forms of surgical therapy. Removal of the spleen in hereditary spherocytosis corrects the main manifestation, anemia.

(10) Enzyme induction. In many inborn errors of metabolism it is likely that a particular enzyme is formed, but because of mutation is a "warped molecule" with, let us say, only 2 per cent of the enzyme activity of its wild-type counterpart. If some method can be found to induce a tenfold increase in the amount of abnormal enzyme produced, although the total enzyme activity is brought only to 20 per cent of the normal, it might make a considerable difference in the functioning of the individual.

Perhaps someday, tailor-made, virus-like agents may be used to change the genetic make-up of human individuals by a process similar to transduction in bacterial genetics. This would indeed be cure! However, it will undoubtedly be easier to influence steps between DNA and the protein that it specifies or to alter the quantitative activity of genes, as suggested above, than to alter the structure of DNA itself.

In the area of therapy genetics also impinges on clinical medicine in connection with the genetic differences in response to drugs—a relatively new area of study in medical genetics called *pharmacogenetics.*

Preventive medicine based on genetic principles can be practiced by discouraging the marriage of two individuals heterozygous for the same "recessive gene." This is being done on the largest scale in Italy where school children are screened for evidence of the heterozygous state of thalassemia (a severe form of anemia) and specifically advised against marriage with another heterozygote. Premarital counselling is a potentially important aspect of genetic practice. One can imagine a stage of development in social organization and in technical methods such that prospective marital partners would be tested for heterozygosity to a considerable number of recessive genes. Even if premarital advice is not taken, it may serve a useful function of permitting early detection of disease in the offspring.

Genetic factors in common diseases

Essentially all diseases can be thought of as constituting a spectrum of the relative importance of genetic and nongenetic factors in their causation. At one end are conditions that are predominantly genetic but not exclusively so, for most disease can be influenced at least slightly by environmental factors. For example, the severity of the clinical changes in phenylketonuria and galactosemia is related to the amount of phenylalanine or galactose in the diet. Common disorders, such as hypertension, atherosclerosis, and peptic ulcer are situated toward the other end of the spectrum where environmental factors predominate. However, genetic factors are also involved; in most of the common conditions the genetic component is probably polygenic.

The genetic basis is usually quite evident in the rarer, more strictly genetic disorders. These are currently being studied in hopes of discovering the precise mode of inheritance, gene frequency, mutation rate, and dynamics in populations. The nature of the "basic" biochemical defect, enzymatic or otherwise, is also being studied. Common multifactorial disorders are being studied to find out if there is a significant genetic factor in the etiology and pathogenesis of the given disorder. The following approaches are used:

(1) Familial aggregation. If a disorder is genetically determined to

a significant extent, then there should be more cases among the relatives of persons with a given disorder than among the relatives of appropriately selected control subjects.

(2) Twin studies. Such studies provide more specific evidence on genetic etiology. In a group of twins with a given disorder, the co-twin in each case is studied to determine whether he is similarly affected or not. On the basis of the findings in the co-twin, the pair is said to be concordant or discordant. If the disorder studied is indeed genetic to a significant extent, then the concordance rate among monozygotic twins should be considerably higher than among dizygotic twins of like sex. The diagnosis of zygosity should be done by objective tests such as blood groups and other markers (p. 52).

(3) Ethnic comparisons. The comparison of frequencies of the given disorder in different ethnic groups may be a clue to the existence of genetic factors. It is not a critical method since one can never be assured of environmental comparability of the groups studied. Often the pertinent environmental factors are not even known.

(4) Blood-group-and-disease association. When demonstrated, this supports the existence of genetic factors; failure to find an association, however, is not evidence against such factors. The classic example is the increased risk of peptic ulcer of the duodenum in persons of blood group O and in persons who are nonsecretors. Persons who are both O and nonsecretors have a risk of peptic ulcer more than double that in the general population.

(5) The study of a possible genetic basis of component mechanisms in a given disorder may help elucidate the genetic basis of the disorder as a whole. For example, fat metabolism and disorders thereof are thought to have some relation to atherosclerosis. Genetic studies of fat metabolism are pertinent, therefore, to the genetics of atherosclerosis.

(6) Animal analogs. Analogs of human diseases occur in some animals; for example, there is a strain of rabbits with high blood pressure. Experimental breeding and other studies not feasible with humans are possible with animals.

References

Jones, F. A., ed., *Clinical Aspects of Genetics*. Philadelphia: J. B. Lippincott Co., 1961.

McKusick, Victor A., "Genetics in Medicine and Medicine in Genetics," *Am. J. Med., 34* (1963), 594-99.

Roberts, J. A. F., *An Introduction to Medical Genetics*, 3rd ed. London: Oxford University Press, 1963.

Genes and Society

The genetic composition of a population has important influences on society, and conversely social structure has important effects on the genetic make-up of a population.

Genetic implications of social forces

The interrelationship of social structure and genetic structure can be illustrated by many examples. Religious and social isolation can result in small endogamous groups even in large cities. The Jews have maintained a certain degree of isolation for many centuries and genetically are demonstrably distinct from the peoples among whom they have lived. Some recessive genes such as those causing pentosuria and Tay-Sachs disease occur almost only in Jews, whereas others such as phenylketonuria are rare in Jews.

Social attitudes toward miscegenation differ widely in different parts of the world. Negro-white assimilation has proceeded relatively rapidly in Brazil, where a tolerant view has prevailed. On the other hand, Negro-white mixing has proceeded more slowly in the southern United States, although after about 10 generations in America the Negro race has reached the point that about 30 per cent of its genes are of European derivation. Possibly the rate of Negro-white admixture in this country has been lower in the last 50 years than it was under conditions of slaveholding in the period before the Emancipation, but exact information on this point is almost impossible to obtain.

Social attitudes toward consanguinity also have important genetic implications. Although the canons of the Roman church do not entirely eliminate consanguinity among its members, there is far less consanguinity in Catholic populations than there is in populations that accept or even favor marriages among blood relations. In some endogamous Moslem groups in India as many as 40 per cent of the marriages are consanguineous. All human societies—with the exception of the Egyptian pharoahs—prohibit parent-offspring and brother-sister matings; this, of course, makes good genetic sense. Other prohibitions that have prevailed in some societies, e.g., that against a man's marrying the wife of a deceased brother, are genetically non-sensical—unless, of course, children affected by an autosomal recessive disorder had occurred from the first mating.

Various social considerations are usually more important in determining the net fertility of a population than is the biological capacity of the population for reproduction. Family planning, birth control, and the prevailing fashions in family size are important factors.

Wars and political upheavals have genetic effects of various types. An interesting rise in the sex ratio—an exaggeration of the usual excess of males over females—is observed during wartime. The sex ratio is higher in offspring born soon after marriage than it is in first offspring born late after marriage. Conception after brief contact may be accompanied by a high sex ratio; this may account for the high sex ratio in wartime.

The expulsion of the Jews from Spain in the fifteenth century and of the Huguenots from France in the fifteenth and sixteenth centuries probably had a significant effect on the genetic constitution and subsequently on the social strength of those countries. Hitler's extermination and expulsion of Jews must inevitably have genetic and consequent social effects.

In summary, social evolution and biologic evolution go hand in hand and are two aspects of an over-all process of development in the human species. Social evolution awaits its Charles Darwin. It is a fascinating view that "ideas are to social evolution what genes are to biological evolution." Mutation, psychosocial selection operating on competing ideas, drift, and flow are forces in social evolution, ideas being the pertinent variable.

Social implications of human genetics

Sewall Wright has suggested that one can usefully think about the social impact of a mutation in terms of a balance between con-

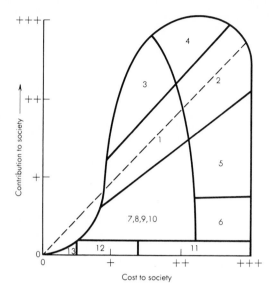

Fig. 10.1. The relationship between the cost and contribution of mutations to society. After Wright, in *The Biological Effects of Atomic Radiation* (National Research Council, 1960).

tribution and cost. His diagram (Fig. 10.1) shows various classes of individuals according to this balance. The diagonal dotted line indicates the average ratio of contribution to cost for the population in question. The ratio may be considered 1 in a static society but as greater than 1 in a society in which there is an advance in well-being in each generation. The several groups indicated by numbers are:

(1) For the bulk of the populations, contribution and cost are balanced at a relatively modest level.

(2) In a second group, cost and contribution are also balanced but at a higher level. Professional people of average competence but with an education and standard of living well above average fall into this group.

(3) Persons who make extraordinary contributions at average cost fall in this group.

(4) In this category are persons who cost society much in terms of education and standard of living but also contribute much more than the average for their level of cost.

(5) Individuals in this class have capacities comparable to those of classes 1 through 4 but contribute less than their cost for reasons such as unearned wealth.

(6) Here Wright puts individuals of normal physical and intellectual capacity whose cost to society outweighs their contribution because of the antisocial nature of their activities: crooks, political demagogues, etc.

In the remaining categories, cost to society definitely outweighs contribution because of physical or mental defects.

(7) Subnormal physical constitution.

(8) Low mentality but not complete helplessness.

(9) Normal to maturity but early physical breakdown by accident, infectious disease, or degenerative disorder.

(10) Mental breakdown after maturity, especially by one of the major psychoses.

(11) Complete physical or mental incapacity throughout a lifetime of more or less normal length.

(12) Death before maturity.

(13) Death *in utero* or soon after birth.

A gene responsible for placing an individual in group 13 is generally viewed as the gravest type of mutation, but its cost to society is less than that of a gene that places its bearer in some other groups, such as 10 or 11.

Nongenetic factors dominate in class 5; the role of genetic factors in class 6 is a matter of uncertainty and disagreement.

Social applications of genetics are illustrated by the use of genetic principles in connection with problems of disputed parentage, particularly disputed paternity. Blood groupings and other marker traits can exclude paternity but cannot establish paternity with absolute certainty, although when some unusual blood groups are found in both father and child the likelihood of paternity can reach a high level of probability. In courts of law of some states such evidence is admitted, whereas in others it is quite illogically not accepted. This legal application is, however, a trivial example of the use of genetic principles, compared to the important areas of eugenics and euphenics.

The eugenics movement had its origin with Galton before the rediscovery of Mendelism. Unfortunately the enthusiasm of the eugenicists has often run ahead of the elucidation of principles on which a sound program must be based. Eugenics can be arbitrarily classified as negative or positive. Negative eugenics is concerned with preventing reproduction of persons carrying undesirable genes. Sterilization and institutionalization are negative eugenic measures. The net result of such measures directed against those genes that are generally agreed to be undesirable is relatively minor, especially when the measures are exercised only on persons homozygous for a particular autosomal recessive gene. In many cases the problem is determining what can indeed be considered undesirable. Negative eugenics is inefficient and often the means by which it is practiced are not ethically acceptable to most people.

Positive eugenics has more practicability than negative eugenics.

No one would dispute the desirability and the scientific soundness of encouraging reproduction of intelligent persons who are an asset to society. For example, income tax relief for university faculties based on number of children would make good sense.

Lederberg has proposed the term *euphenics* as a counterpart of eugenics; in a sense eugenics and euphenics are comparable to the parallel terms *phenotype* and *genotype*. Eugenics concerns itself with "improvement" in the genetic material. Euphenics would concern itself with influencing the chain of information from DNA to RNA to protein to attain a more desirable phenotype. It is almost certain that in the not-too-distant future there will be a rapid development of methods for controlling the phenotype by influencing the gene-controlled developmental processes that are just beginning to be understood. Two areas of possible development are control of the size and capacity of the brain and modification of the immunologic barriers to organ transplantation ("spare parts" surgery).

References

Coon, Carleton S., *The Story of Man*, 2nd ed. New York: Alfred A. Knopf, Inc., 1962.

Haller, M. H., *Eugenics: Hereditarian Attitudes in American Thought*. New Brunswick: Rutgers University Press, 1963.

Lederberg, Joshua, "Molecular Biology, Eugenics and Euphenics," *Nature, 198* (1963), 428-29.

National Academy of Sciences, *The Biological Effects of Atomic Radiation*. Washington, D.C.: National Research Council, 1960.

A Guide to Further Reading

General sources

Boyer, S. H., IV, ed., *Papers on Human Genetics*. Englewood Cliffs, N.J.: Prentice-Hall, Inc., 1963.

Carter, C. O., *Human Heredity*. Baltimore: Penguin Books, Inc., 1962.

Penrose, Lionel S., *Outline of Human Genetics*, 2nd ed. London: William Heinemann, Ltd., 1963.

Roberts, J. A. F., *An Introduction to Medical Genetics*, 3rd ed. London: Oxford University Press, 1963.

Stern, Curt, *Principles of Human Genetics*, 2nd ed. San Francisco: W. H. Freeman & Company, Publishers, 1960.

Biochemical genetics

Garrod, Archibald E., *Inborn Errors of Metabolism*. Reprinted with a supplement by Harry Harris. London: Oxford University Press, 1963.

Human cytogenetics

Montagu, M. F. A., ed., *Genetic Mechanisms in Human Disease: Chromosomal Aberrations*. Springfield, Ill.: Charles C Thomas, Publisher, 1961.

Statistical genetics

Li, C. C., *Human Genetics*. New York: McGraw-Hill Book Company, 1961.

Periodicals for keeping up with the rapidly advancing field of human genetics

American Journal of Human Genetics (published quarterly by the American Society of Human Genetics).

Annals of Human Genetics (published quarterly by the Galton Laboratory, London).

Journal of Chronic Diseases. Annual reviews of human genetics prepared by the staff of the Division of Medical Genetics, The Johns Hopkins University, appear each year (beginning 1958) in one monthly issue of this journal. The reviews are collected in three-year periods in a bound volume, e.g., McKusick, Victor A., *et al.*, *Medical Genetics 1958-1960*. St. Louis: The C. V. Mosby Company, 1961.

Steinberg, Arthur G., and Alexander G. Bearn, eds., *Progress in Medical Genetics*. New York: Grune & Stratton, Inc., 1961 (Vol. I), 1962 (Vol. II), and 1964 (Vol. III). A collection of long reviews in specific areas of human genetics.

Index

143